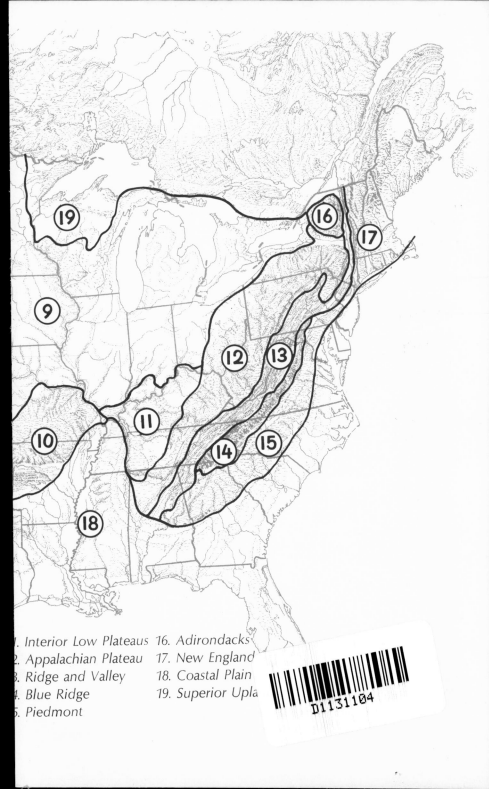

FIELD GUIDE TO LANDFORMS IN THE UNITED STATES

FIELD GUIDE TO

DRAWINGS BY GENEVIEVE SHIMER

SECTIONS AND LANDFORM MAPS BY ERWIN RAISZ

OTHER BOOKS BY JOHN A. SHIMER

This Sculptured Earth
This Changing Earth:
    An Introduction to Geology
Graphic Methods in Structural Geology
    (with W. L. Donn)

LANDFORMS
IN THE
UNITED STATES

John A. Shimer

The Macmillan Company, New York, New York

Collier-Macmillan Ltd., London

The Macmillan Company
866 Third Avenue, New York, N.Y. 10022
Collier-Macmillan Canada Ltd., Toronto, Ontario

Library of Congress Catalog Card Number: 75-141935
Second Printing 1972
Printed in the United States of America

Contents

Preface   XV

I *GEOLOGIC PROVINCES*

1   Basis of Subdivision   3
2   The Coastal Plain   7
3   Piedmont   16
4   Blue Ridge   21
5   Ridge and Valley   24
6   Appalachian Plateau   30
7   New England   35
8   Adirondacks   41
9   Interior Low Plateaus   44
10 Central Lowlands   48
11 The Great Plains   58
12 Interior Highlands   65
13 Superior Upland   69
14 Rocky Mountains   72
15 Colorado Plateau   88
16 Columbia Plateau   98
17 Basin and Range   104
18 Sierra Nevada   110

75542

19	Cascades	113
20	Pacific Border	116
21	Alaska	123
22	Hawaiian Islands	132

II *LANDSCAPE FEATURES*

23	Rock Types and Structures	139
24	Igneous Rock Landscapes	152
25	Glaciated Landscapes	159
26	River Features	170
27	Coastal Features	182
28	Desert Forms	191
29	Rock Scultpture: Shapes and Slopes	196
30	Limestone Caves and Ground Water	209
31	Lakes and Swamps	213
32	Mountains	219
33	Man and the Earth	223

Detailed Landform Maps of the United States, with Boundary Lines of the Geologic Provinces	229
Landform Summary Chart	258
Further Reading	264
Index	266

PHOTOGRAPHS

Monument Valley, Utah	5
New York City and Long Island	11
Hudson River, Bear Mountain Area, New York	18
Great Smokies and Fontana Lake, North Carolina	22
Ridges and Valleys in Central Pennsylvania	28
Catskill Mountains from the East	32
Coast of Maine, Casco Bay Area	39
Lake Placid, Adirondack Mountains, New York	42
White River, Indiana	55
Great Plains, South Dakota	62
Lakes in Northern Wisconsin	70
Front Range of the Rocky Mountains, Colorado	74
Beartooth Mountains, Montana	80
The Grand Tetons, Wyoming	83
The Grand Canyon, Arizona	93
Bryce Canyon, Utah	94
"Dry Falls" Grand Coulee, Washington	102
Death Valley, California	108-109

Sierra Nevada   112
The Three Sisters, Oregon   114
Sea Cliffs and Terrace on Oregon Coast   121
Chugach Range, Alaska   125
The White Mountains, Alaska   126
Arctic Coastal Plain, Alaska   129
Kilauea Caldera, Hawaii   134
Na Pali Cliffs, Kauai   135

MAPS AND CHARTS

Geologic Time Chart   xi
Location Map of Geologic Structure Sections   xii
Areas of Glacial Features in the United States   52-53
Areas of Igneous Rock in the United States   158
Detailed Landform Maps of the United States   230-257
Landform Summary Chart   258

Geologic Time Chart

ERA	PERIOD	EPOCH	
CENOZOIC (*0–60 million years ago*)	Quaternary	Recent Pleistocene	"Ice Age"
	Tertiary	Pliocene Miocene Oligocene Eocene Paleocene	Rocky Mountains formed
MESOZOIC (*60–230 million years ago*)	Cretaceous Jurassic Triassic		
PALEZOIC (*230–600 million years ago*)	Permian Pennsylvanian Mississippian Devonian Silurian Ordovician Cambrian		Appalachian Mountains formed

PRECAMBRIAN
(*over 600 million years ago*)

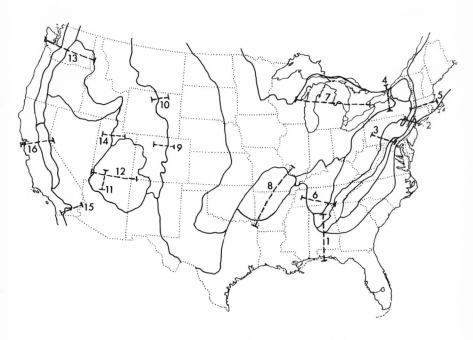

GEOLOGIC STRUCTURE SECTIONS

1	Coastal Plain	Pensacola–Birmingham
2	Piedmont	Delaware River–N.Y.C.–Long Island
3	Appalachian Mountains	Altoona–Gettysburg
4	Appalachian Plateau	Finger Lakes–Lake Ontario–Canada
5	New England	Catskill Mountains–Boston
6	Interior Low Plateaus	Tennessee River–Nashville–Blue Ridge
7	Central Lowlands	Green Bay–Toronto
8	Interior Highlands	Texarkana–Saint Louis
9	Rocky Mountains	Park Range–Front Range–Great Plains
10	Rocky Mountains	Bighorn Mountains
11	Colorado Plateau	Williams–Grand Canyon–Bryce Canyon
12	Colorado Plateau	Southern Utah, West–East
13	Columbia Plateau	Olympic Mountains–Lake Coeur d'Alene
14	Basin and Range	Great Salt Lake–Wasatch Mountains
15	Basin and Range	Salton Sea
16	Pacific Border	San Francisco–Lake Tahoe

Preface

In the United States there are notable differences in the landscape between one region and another. Some areas are characterized by gently rounded landforms and relatively slow-moving streams; some, by deep canyons, rapid swirling water, and precipitous cliffs; and still others by land so flat that one looks in vain to the horizon for the slightest visible undulation in the surface. Coastal scenery varies from steep rock cliffs plunging directly into the sea to wide tracts of salt-water marshes and deep estuaries to extensive sand beaches and bars which border some coasts. Thus each region of the country has its own "flavor," its own set of characteristic landforms.

Each specific landscape is, in its details, unique. However, a discerning eye soon notes similarities among various scenes, such as in the shapes of hills as seen against the sky, the slopes of the valleys and their various modifications, the color and type of rock, and the arrangement of hills and ridges and their intervening valleys. Similarity in landforms is explained by their similar history.

Part I of this guide briefly describes the topography of each of the major geologic divisions of the country. A map of these is reproduced on the end papers. A number of geologic structure sections, drawn to show the relationship between surface topography and underlying rock masses, are included in Part I.

Part II discusses and illustrates some of the most common scenic features which collectively give any landscape its unique character.

The detailed landform maps in Part II are reproduced with the kind permission of Ginn and Company. Erwin Raisz drew these maps to accompany *The Physiographic Provinces of North America* by W. W. Atwood, Ginn and Company, Boston, 1940.

I

GEOLOGIC PROVINCES

1 | *Basis of Subdivision*

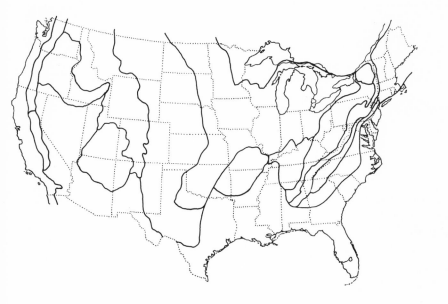

Continental United States can be divided into three major parts. Mountainous terrain is found in both the East and the West, with a generally subdued plains area in between. These major divisions, in turn, can be subdivided into smaller, more easily discussed, units—the geologic provinces. (See inserts at the end of the book.)

The family resemblances among the landscape features in any one geologic province are explainable in terms of a common geologic history. The rock type, its structure, and the amount and kinds of weathering and erosion are more or less uniform throughout an area, such as, for example, the Coastal Plain or the Appalachian Plateau or the Colorado Plateau.

Differences between one part of a province and another can be explained by minor variations in history, structure, or rock type. Such a division of the country into geologic provinces allows one to make the greatest number of generally valid statements about an area before the necessity of mentioning exceptions.

Some boundaries between provinces are very obvious and abrupt, such as that between the flat plains and the Rocky Mountains in Colorado or that between the Blue Ridge of Virginia and the Great Valley to its west. Boundaries, in places, may interfinger one with another, and in some cases, erosion may cause remnants of one type of landform to be left as outliers in another area. Remnants of the higher parts of the Appalachian Plateau appear as isolated erosional remnants, called knobs in Kentucky and Tennessee. Many boundaries between provinces and subprovinces are gradational in nature and may not be easily noticed. That between the Central Lowlands and the Great Plains is arbitrary along much of its length. Furthermore, in places, structures and topographic characteristics of one province are found as isolated patches in a neighboring one. For instance, although the Black Hills belong both structurally and scenically with the Rocky Mountains, they can most conveniently be discussed as a subprovince of the "host" province, the Great Plains in this case.

An understanding of how variations in type of rock, structure, and geologic history can lead to such prominent differences in landforms is based on comprehension of fundamental geologic processes and an appreciation of the truly transient nature of the earth's crust when considered in terms of the time available for geologic change, time measured in millions and hundreds of millions of years. With such a time span, the day-to-day, apparently insignificant geologic events become cumulatively of great importance, and it can be appreciated that the landscape as we see it today is but a glimpse of an ever-evolving

MONUMENT VALLEY, UTAH. Horizontal layers and an even skyline are characteristic of the Colorado Plateau. (Photo by Dorothy Abbe)

earth whose present surface has come about through modification of a former surface and will change into something new in the future. Given time, the loftiest mountains will be destroyed by the same forces which cause the frost-heaving of a sidewalk, the crumbling of a bit of masonry, or the washing out of a newly seeded lawn.

The processes of weathering cause the breakup of solid rocks at the earth's surface into mud, sand, gravel, and various soluble compounds. The agents of erosion—wind, waves, rivers, ground water, and glaciers—then pick up and transport this debris, eventually dumping it into diversely shaped piles and layers of sediments. The erosional agents are constantly aided in their job of transportation by the direct force of gravity, which pulls any loose material downslope, sometimes rapidly, as in rockfalls and landslides, and sometimes slowly, as in soil creep.

Igneous activity and mountain building are opposed to the destructive aspects of weathering and erosion, leading to the production of mountains and highlands. In igneous activity, earth materials move as hot liquids to appear as lava flows or cones at the surface or to cool into variously shaped, intrusive bodies underneath the surface.

Folding, faulting, and the warping of the earth's layers either up or down are aspects of mountain building. Formerly horizontal layers may now be found folded and tilted, and once-continuous layers, offset by faulting.

Natural scenery thus results from the unceasing interaction, extending over hundreds of millions of years, between the destructive forces of wind, water, and weather (gradation) and the counterconstructive forces of igneous activity and the uplift of the land associated with folding and faulting (mountain building).

Sculpturing of the land by the forces of gradation occurs on all scales from that of a mountain range to the small-scale irregularities a fraction of an inch across on the surface of a rock. Diversity in landforms comes about from variations in type of rock, the structures they have taken, and the amount and type of weathering and erosion which have carved them.

Man, in his work of earth sculpture, generally confines himself to the redistribution of already-formed loose debris which thinly mantles the solid rock of the crust. More rarely, but to an ever-increasing degree, he aids the agents of weathering when he blasts bedrock in the production of tunnels, roads, canals, and mines.

2 | The Coastal Plain

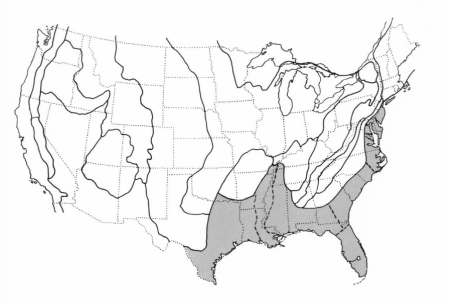

The Coastal Plain extends for 2,200 miles from Cape Cod to the Mexican border and then for an additional 1,000 miles along the Gulf coast of Mexico. The underwater, seaward extension, called the continental shelf, varies in width from a few miles to over 200 miles along the North Atlantic coast. North of Cape Cod, there is no Coastal Plain; it has been entirely covered by the sea. As a whole the plain is underlain by poorly consolidated sediments, Cretaceous to Recent in age, which dip gently seaward.

It is an area of generally low relief, measured in a few tens of feet with, in places, some of the major hills and ridges rising from 200 to 300 feet above their surroundings. The more

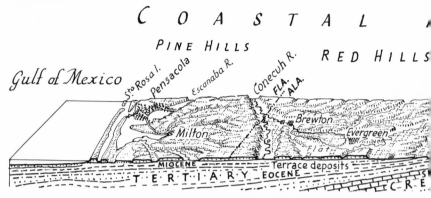

South

C O A S T A L

PINE HILLS

RED HILLS

Gulf of Mexico

Sto Rosa I.

Pensacola

Escanaba R.

Conecuh R.

FLA.

ALA.

Brewton

Evergreen

Milton

Flat

MIOCENE

Terrace deposits

T E R T I A R Y   EOCENE

C R E

COASTAL PLAIN, PENSACOLA—BIRMINGHAM.

resistant layers, often the sandy ones, project as erosional remnants and form low, elongated, asymmetric ridges, or cuestas, parallel to the coastline. The steeper slope of these features faces inland.

Geologically, the most recently formed features lie along the coast. They are wave-cut cliffs, beaches, sand spits, bars, and, in many places, sand dunes built up by the wind. Away from the sea, the landforms are mostly stream-fashioned.

CAPE COD TO NORTH CAROLINA*

From Cape Cod to the south end of Pamlico Sound in North Carolina, a marked rise in sea level has caused the inundation of the lower reaches of many major rivers to produce easily notable estuaries, such as New York Harbor, Delaware Bay, Chesapeake Bay, and Albemarle and Pamlico sounds. The flooding has resulted in the semiisolation of broad peninsular tracts. From Cape Cod to as far south as the James River in Virginia,

* See key map at beginning of chapter.

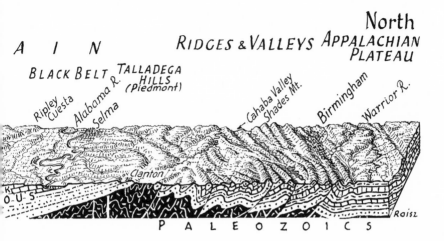

North
RIDGES & VALLEYS APPALACHIAN
PLATEAU
A   I   N
BLACK BELT TALLADEGA
HILLS
(Piedmont)

Ripley Cuesta
Alabama R.
Selma
Clanton
Cahaba Valley
Shades Mt.
Birmingham
Warrior R.
O-U-S
Raisz
P   A   L   E   O   Z   O   I   C   S

the submergence was such that the ocean reached in as far as the Fall Zone, that is, the contact between harder and older rocks of the Piedmont province and the younger, softer rocks of the Coastal Plain.

The original preglacial topography of both Cape Cod and Long Island has been drastically modified by glacial action. The major part of Cape Cod consists of glacial deposits. The Sandwich Moraine runs roughly east-west and is joined at its western end by the Buzzard's Bay Moraine, which trends toward the southwest to include the Elizabeth Islands. Morainal topography is typically hummocky with many kettle holes, some of which are now filled with water. An outwash plain, pitted with many kettle holes, extends southward from the junction between the two moraines. Postglacial action by the sea has formed many beaches; a number of sand spits, notably those at Provincetown and Monomoy; and various sea cliffs, such as those on the easternmost bulge of the cape.

Long Island also is composed essentially of two morainal ridges at the north and outwash material at the south (see Raisz

Structure, Section 2). The Ronkonkoma Moraine extends into Montauk Point before it dips under the sea, and the Harbor Hill Moraine at the north causes the elongation of the island into Orient Point. At the western end of Long Island, the two moraines coincide, having here the greatest elevation, somewhat over 400 feet. South of the morainal tract is the outwash plain, sloping gently to disappear under the present level of the sea. Waves and currents have formed, and are continually modifying, the extensive sand deposits on the south side, such as Coney Island, Rockaway, and Fire Island. Toward the eastern end of the island, wave erosion is more noticeable, having formed small wave-cut cliffs. It has been estimated that the area of Long Island would be approximately one-fourth of what it is now if all the glacial deposits were removed.

Long Island Sound marks the location of a drowned valley cut into soft layers between the hard metamorphic and igneous rocks of Connecticut and the cuesta underlying the glacial debris on the north side of Long Island. Further evidence of this drowning is obvious in the presence of many short estuaries which indent both the north and south sides of Long Island.

Along the coast of New Jersey and south of Chesapeake Bay, offshore bars are especially conspicuous. They almost enclose Albemarle and Pamlico sounds. If there is no change in sea level, the sounds and estuaries behind the sand bars will eventually become filled in with sediments and organic growth.

NORTH CAROLINA TO FLORIDA

From Pamlico Sound to Florida, the submergence of the Coastal Plain has been less than that in the north, and in place of the extensive development of offshore bars, there is a series of islands along the coast. Furthermore, the inner zone, next to the Piedmont, is somewhat more hilly than the similar area to the north.

The islands along the coast here have apparently three different origins. Some are erosional remnants, or higher land now isolated by a slight rise in sea level, some are low marsh islands, and some are composed of arcuate wave-deposited sand ridges.

The Carolina bays, especially noticeable from the air, are

NEW YORK CITY AND LONG ISLAND. (Aero Service Division—Litton Industries)

striking features in this part of the Coastal Plain. Especially abundant in Virginia and North and South Carolina, these mysterious features are slightly oval, shallow depressions and are very irregular in size, ranging from a few tens of feet to hundreds of feet across. Their distribution appears to be random in that they are found in all types and ages of Coastal Plain sediments. Usually they are elongated in a northwest–southeast direction. It has been estimated that there may be as many as one-half million of them. Some geologists ascribe their origin to showers of meteorites which all came from the same general direction. However, the fact that they are confined to the Coastal Plain seems to rule out this extraterrestrial origin, and many other theories of origin have been suggested, ranging from being various types of solution depressions to extinct marine lagoons formed on the Coastal Plain as it rose from the sea. There is still no generally accepted theory as to origin.

FLORIDA

The emergence of Florida from under the sea has been very recent. The Everglades and Lake Okeechobee, once depressions on the sea floor, now mark slightly lower areas on the land, much of which is less than 20 feet above sea level. The heavy rainfall and the flat land inevitably lead to extensive swampy areas.

Limestone is widespread in the northern parts of Florida, which has resulted in the extensive development of sinkholes. Drainage is largely via underground passageways, and springs of large volume abound. Silver Springs is one of the largest, with a daily flow in excess of half a billion gallons. At a number of places, springs have emerged at the side of a sinkhole, and by sapping—that is, undercutting the wall by solution—have extended the sinks into steep-walled alcoves or recesses.

Unlike many other karst areas in the United States, most of the Florida sinkholes extend below the water table and have water at their bottoms. The underground passageways are well connected, forming a fine artesian system. Several springs discharge on the sea floor a number of miles offshore.

At the southern end of Florida, a series of islands, the Keys, extends for 150 miles to Key West. The easternmost group is part of a former coral reef, and the western group, also composed of limestone, marks the higher parts of a shoal in the sea. This latter group extends for about 40 miles from East Bahia Honda Key to Key West.

Action by waves and currents has greatly modified the coastline. In some places uplifted marine terraces are obvious, marking former stands of the sea. One of the most striking features connected with changed sea level is Trail Ridge in northern Florida. Essentially a sand bar, this has a length of 130 miles and stands well above its present surroundings.

EAST GULF SECTION

The Coastal Plain between Florida and the Mississippi River flood plain has many of the same types of features found north of Florida, but the emphasis on topographic forms is somewhat changed. The Coastal Plain is slightly wider here, and a greater difference in resistance between various layers has resulted in the development of a much more marked series of cuestas and intervening valleys. Such a development has produced what is called a belted Coastal Plain. Along the coast the belted character changes to a zone of sea-formed terraces and, along the shore itself, to a widespread development of spits and bars.

Characteristically, a Coastal Plain cuesta, most obvious when viewed from the landward side, appears to be composed of a series of hills. The cuesta from the seaward side is far less obvious, as the slope of the land to the crest is much less steep.

From central Alabama westward, the rocks are not resistant enough to cause a series of rapids and falls as the Piedmont rocks do to the east.

MISSISSIPPI RIVER ALLUVIAL PLAIN

The Coastal Plain reaches its widest development where the Mississippi River, with its broad alluvial plain, extends inland as far as Cairo, Illinois. This valley, where river sediments cover any underlying material, has many abandoned channels, oxbow lakes, and wide, marshy, flood-plain flats. It extends southward until it merges with the present delta plain at approximately the head of the Atchafalaya River, one of the major streams of the present delta area. The Mississippi River has constantly varied its course here as the meanders shift their positions outward and downstream. An air view shows a complex pattern of low arcuate ridges and intervening low areas, marking former positions of the continually shifting river.

The alluvial valley varies in width from about 25 miles near Natchez to 125 miles, its widest, near Helena, Arkansas. The valley sides are marked by prominent bluffs which rise from 100 to 200 feet above the valley floor. A thick coating of loess is obvious along the bluff zone in many places.

The essentially flat floor of the valley is interrupted at the north by Crowley's Ridge, which protrudes about 200 feet. This ridge extends in a north-south direction, more-or-less continuously, for about 200 miles from a point near Commerce, Missouri, to Helena, Arkansas. At the south there are smaller erosional remnants, such as Macon Ridge, Bastrop Hills, and Sicily Island.

The history in this part of the Coastal Plain alternates between deposition of a flood plain at times of higher sea level and erosion at times of lowered sea level. Terraces of former valley fill have been left along the sides of the present valley.

The Mississippi River delta consists, as a whole, of a number of smaller separate deltas, each built when the river had a different exit to the sea than at present. The current, actively growing delta was initiated between 400 and 500 years ago. This has now been built out so far that if man doesn't intervene, a newer and shorter course to the sea will soon be taken via the Atchafalaya River. The present path of the Mississippi River to the sea from the junction of the Atchafalaya River is 300 miles compared with the 140 miles via the Atchafalaya.

In the lower reaches of the Mississippi River area, the relief of the land is a very few feet at most, the major elevations being the natural levees which border the principal channels.

WEST GULF SECTION

West of the Mississippi River, the Coastal Plain shows the same features that are found in the east Gulf section. Cuesta ridges with intervening lowlands roughly parallel the coast, giving it a belted appearance also. In the coastal zone there are a number of estuaries and a few alluvial valleys and associated deltas, offshore bars, and lagoons.

Along southeast Louisiana and eastern Texas, the coastal zone is characterized by a complex of relict beach ridges which lies roughly parallel with the present coastline. In contrast, the west Texas coastal area from Galveston to the Mexican border is an almost-continuous line of barrier sand islands in front of a somewhat-embayed coastline. Such offshore bars are often composed of a number of parallel ridges, and in many places, the wind has redeposited the sand into dunes extending 50 or more feet above the sea.

The inner margin of the west Texas area from Austin to the Rio Grande is marked by the Balcones Escarpment, formed by an uplift along the Balcones Fault.

3 | Piedmont

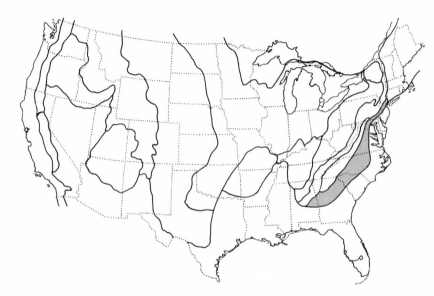

The Piedmont province extends from the Hudson River to
Alabama. It lies next to the Coastal Plain and is the easternmost
of the four sections into which the Appalachian highlands are
divided. These sections—Piedmont, Blue Ridge, Ridge and Valley, and Appalachian Plateau—are essentially parallel one with
the other and trend roughly northeast to southwest. The New
England area, in many respects, is a continuation of the same
type of topography which is found in the Piedmont and Blue
Ridge areas further south. However, it is most conveniently
treated as a separate province because of its somewhat isolated
position and the great modification that glacial erosion and
deposition have wrought there.

The Piedmont, not including the Triassic subsections, along with the Blue Ridge province to the west, is composed mainly of metamorphic rocks intruded by various igneous rocks. The structure is complex, with many faults and folds. In width it varies from approximately 10 miles at the narrowest to 125 miles near the Virgina—North Carolina border, and is the least rugged of all the Appalachian highlands provinces. The inland margin increases in elevation from about 200 feet in New Jersey to over 1,800 feet in Georgia. Such a rise coincides roughly with a greater distance from the sea.

In general, the igneous and metamorphic rocks of the Piedmont are more resistant to erosion than the sediments of the Coastal Plain on the east, which explains the presence of falls or rapids along many of the rivers which cross from one province to another. This Fall Line, topographically, is most distinctive north of the Potomac River. Here, the Piedmont rises abruptly 100 to 200 feet over the general level of the Coastal Plain. Further south, the junction is less obvious. Notable Fall-Line cities are Philadelphia, Baltimore, Washington, Richmond, Raleigh, Columbia, and Macon.

On the west, the Piedmont is bordered by the more rugged and higher-standing rocks of the Blue Ridge province. Toward the north the crystalline rocks of the Piedmont taper into a point which terminates at Trenton, New Jersey. An area of Triassic sediments with included lava flows and sills continues the Piedmont into northern New Jersey opposite New York City and, in this fashion, connects the Piedmont with the New England province, two extensions of which, the Manhattan prong on the east and the Reading prong on the west, enclose the northern part of the New Jersey Triassic area.

Near the Blue Ridge on the western margin, a number of monadnocks rise above the general level of the Piedmont. These are most noticeable from Virginia southward. Examples are Big Cobbler in Virginia; Brushy, South, and Kings mountains

NW

RIDGES & VALLEYS

NEW JERSEY HIGHLANDS
(PIEDMONT)

POCONO PLATEAU

Port Jervis
Delaware R.
KITTATINNY MTS.

GREAT VALLEY

POCHUC MTS.

WAWAYANDA PLATEAU

Greenwood L.

Wanaque Res.

TRIAS

RAMAPO FRONT

Suffern

W

High Point
2023

Sussex

RAMAPO Mts.

DEVONIAN SILURIAN ORDOVICIAN

Lava

FOLDED PALEOZOICS   METAMORPHICS   TRIASSIC SS. & LA

PIEDMONT, DELAWARE RIVER—N.Y.C.—LONG ISLAND.

HUDSON RIVER, BEAR MOUNTAIN AREA, NEW YORK. The lowlands toward the north, at the top of the picture, lie in the Ridge and Valley province. The highlands which cross the Hudson here belong to the Reading prong, an extension of resistant rocks from New England. (Skyviews)

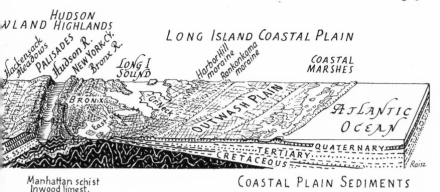

HUDSON
NLAND HIGHLANDS
Hackensack meadows
PALISADES
Hudson R.
NEW YORK CY.
Bronx R.
LONG I SOUND
LONG ISLAND COASTAL PLAIN
Harbor Hill moraine
Ronkonkoma moraine
COASTAL MARSHES
BRONX
East
Creek
OUTWASH PLAIN
ATLANTIC OCEAN
QUATERNARY
TERTIARY
CRETACEOUS
Raisz

Manhattan schist
Inwood limest.

COASTAL PLAIN SEDIMENTS

in North Carolina; and Stone Mountain and Findley Ridge in Georgia. Otherwise, the surface of the Piedmont is rolling with only moderately deeply incised valleys in the western parts becoming shallower toward the Coastal Plain.

A deep residual soil, up to 100 feet thick in places, characteristically covers the bedrock. This indicates a long exposure to chemical weathering with moderately slow removal of the weathered products. Granite is widespread, especially in the southern Piedmont. Stone Mountain, Georgia, is a mile-and-a-half-long granite exfoliation dome which stands 650 feet above its surroundings.

The Triassic subsections form lower parts of the Piedmont because of their generally less-resistant rocks; sandstone and shale. These areas are elongated, down-faulted basins which extend intermittently from New York through New Jersey, Pennsylvania, Maryland, Virginia, and North Carolina. (See Raisz Structure, Section 3.) The sandstone and shale are characteristically deep red in color and are interbedded with basalt lava flows with, in places, intruded sills. The sedimentary layers are tilted, and the more resistant flows and sills stand out as prominent ridges. The Palisades of New York and New Jersey mark the outcrop of a sill, in places 1,000 feet thick, tilted westward, and the Watchung Mountains are formed of lava flows which were interbedded with the sediments and then exposed after the whole sequence was uptilted and uncovered by erosion. Such ridges characteristically have a steep scarp face and a gentler dip slope. The southeast-facing scarps of the Watchung Mountains are as much as 400 feet above their surroundings. Basalt dikes of Triassic age are also found intruding the crystallines (granites and metamorphics) away from the Triassic basins themselves.

4 | Blue Ridge

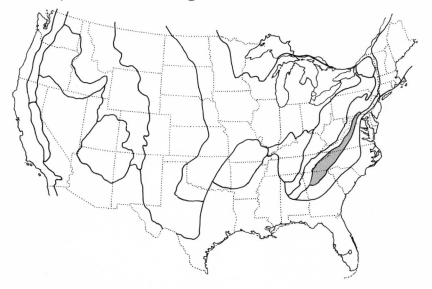

This province extends from Carlisle, Pennsylvania, 550 miles southward into Georgia. North of Roanoke, Virginia, it is distinctly narrower than it is farther south, and for long distances is a single ridge which, for most of its length, stands a few hundred to a few thousand feet above its surroundings.

South of Roanoke, the province is much broader, is higher, and is composed of many heterogeneously distributed mountains over 6,000 feet high. The peaks here, compared with the angular glaciated mountains of the West, are rounded and more subdued in aspect. Mount Mitchell, 6,684 feet in elevation, is the highest point in the Appalachian highlands and lies in this section. The southern Blue Ridge is notable for having a very

GREAT SMOKIES AND FONTANA LAKE. This is an artificial lake. (Photograph © 1968 by Charles E. Rotkin. From *The U.S.A.: An Aerial Close-up* [Crown])

straight and high eastward-facing scarp, which marks the junction with the Piedmont. Near Roanoke, this scarp is 2,500 feet high, increasing in elevation to a maximum of 4,000 feet near Blowing Rock, North Carolina.

Throughout its length, the province has a very clear and marked boundary on the west, where a wide and continuous lowland, the Great Valley, cut into soft, early-Paleozoic sediments, lies between the folded and faulted metamorphic and igneous rocks of the Blue Ridge and the first ridge of the Ridge and Valley province. (See Raisz Structure, Section 3.)

Along the northwest side of the Great Smokies, features known as coves are found. They are relatively flat-floored, small valleys a few square miles in area, which mark extensions of the Great Valley topography and rock types into the crystalline regions of the Blue Ridge.

5 | Ridge and Valley

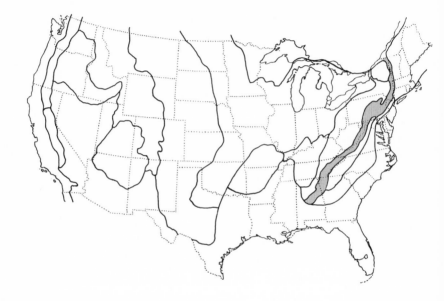

This province extends 1,200 miles from the Saint Lawrence River lowland to Alabama and varies in width from a very few miles to as many as 80 in central Pennsylvania. The region is characterized by linear ridges which trend northeast to southwest. In places, these parallel each other for long distances; in others, they diverge, converge, or make S-bends. The ridge-makers are predominantly sandstone and conglomerate, the lowlands being underlain by shale and limestone. The topography is typical of that of eroded folded rocks.

From the air the landscape is distinctive and striking. The ridges, which are usually wooded, extend to the horizon and appear like ordered wave crests separated by relatively broad, flat troughs. Many of the lowlands, in contrast with the ridges, have been cleared, showing an ordered arrangement of fields and roads. Each ridge shows numerous parallel corrugations down its flanks. They mark the courses of the many streams feeding the slower-moving rivers which flow through the valleys parallel to the ridges. Here and there a major stream may be seen cutting across the linear structure. Where it crosses a ridge, a narrow water gap is formed. Wind gaps, or low saddles, across the otherwise even-crested ridges are visible on closer inspection.

The remarkably uniform elevations of the ridge tops have been explained as being parts of a former widespread erosion surface, or peneplain. This surface was uplifted, and the ensuing renewed erosion has now cut the extensive valley system between the ridges. The wind gaps, now often used as passes across the ridges, mark former water gaps present in the earlier cycle of erosion. They are now left high and dry following the uplift and consequent renewed erosion of the region.

An eastern series of valleys, called the Great Valley or Appalachian Valley, is parallel with the general trend of the structure, collectively making a more-or-less continuous lowland tract along most of the length of the province. From north to south the following valleys belong to this lowland: Lake Champlain, part of the Hudson River, the Walkill, Lebanon, Cumberland, Hagerstown and Shenandoah rivers, valley of eastern Tennessee, and Coosa River. The width of the lowland, which separates the first major ridge of the province from the next eastern province, varies from 2 to 50 miles.

The western parts of the province are characterized by the ridges which vary in number from section to section.

At the north end, the Lake Champlain–Hudson River part of the province is bounded on the west by the high-standing Adirondack, Catskill, and Pocono mountains. On the east lies the New England area, which includes the Green and Taconic

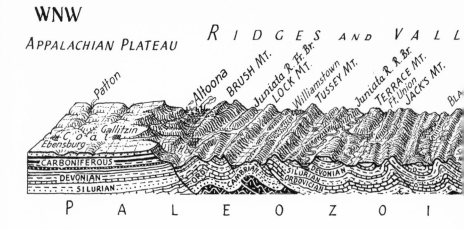

APPALACHIAN MOUNTAINS, ALTOONA–GETTYSBURG.

mountains and the highlands of the Hudson River. (See Raisz Structure, Section 5.)

Only one obvious ridge is present in this section, and that appears only in the southern third of the area. It is called the Shawangunk Mountain in New York State and Kittatinny Mountain in New Jersey. (See Raisz Structure, Section 2.) Otherwise the area is essentially a lowland. Minor ridges, with widths measured in a few tens of feet rather than in hundreds and with lengths measured in a few miles rather than in tens of miles, do, however, appear. These are masked somewhat by glacial deposits which have deranged the preglacial drainage to produce lakes and swamps.

The Hudson River leaves this section as it cuts across the resistant rocks of the Reading prong of the New England province at the Bear Mountain area.

The middle section of the Ridge and Valley province extends through Pennsylvania and Maryland and along the border country between West Virginia and Virginia. It is bounded on the west by a very prominent escarpment, marking the eastern margin of the Appalachian Plateau province. In Pennsylvania,

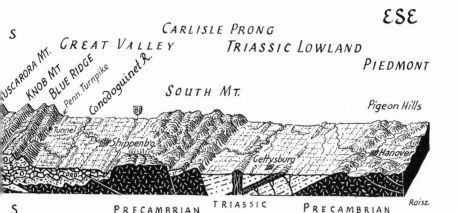

the scarp, called the Allegheny Front, reaches an elevation of 1,800 feet at Altoona.

The development of zigzag ridges from the erosion of plunging folds is especially notable in central Pennsylvania, where the folded belt reaches its maximum width of 80 miles. The ridges are, in general, closer together than in the southern section, and the remarkably even crests of the ridge tops are very obvious. Here also, there is an ideal development of the trellis drainage pattern.

In Virginia, the Great Valley, divided into two parts by Massanutten Mountain, is underlain by extensive areas of limestone. Many sinkholes, disappearing streams, and caves are found, such as Luray, Endless, Shenandoah, and Massanutten. Natural Bridge and Natural Tunnel, both due to the solution of limestone, lie in the southern part of Virginia. Natural Bridge is probably a roof remnant of a former underground river channel, now exposed except for one remaining part, and Natural Tunnel, about 900 feet long, is a feature where somewhat more of the underground passageway still remains.

Surface outcrops of limestone show well-developed etched,

grooved, or pitted surfaces, so-called lapiés. In places, a slightly more resistant, dipping limestone layer can be seen extending for long distances across the fields. The line of outcrops shows very clearly the consistent orientation of a specific layer, everywhere parallel with the general trend of the Great Valley.

In the southern part of the Ridge and Valley province in Tennessee, Georgia, and Alabama, the ridges are not as numerous as in the middle section, and the division into an eastern valley and a western ridge section is not obvious. The ridges here are generally homoclinal in structure, the anticlinal and synclinal ridges of the middle section being generally lacking. (See Raisz Structure, Section 6.)

RIDGES AND VALLEYS IN CENTRAL PENNSYLVANIA. The ridges are wooded, and the lowlands show an intricate pattern of cleared fields. The Pennsylvania Turnpike is the major northeast–southwest road at the bottom of the photograph. Note where it tunnels through Tuscarora Mountain. (Aero Service Division—Litton Industries)

6 | *Appalachian Plateau*

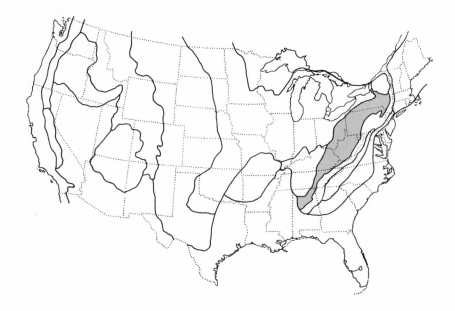

As seen from the air, this area resembles a very choppy sea of small mountains with slopes pointed toward every direction of the compass. There is a striking contrast between the plateau scenery and the Ridge and Valley area immediately to the east, where the majestic sequence of parallel ridges and valleys dominates the scene.

Relief in the plateau is measured in hundreds of feet to over a thousand feet. Hill slopes are steep, and roads for this reason are apt to wind along tops of ridges or follow major valleys. They thus reflect in their pattern the valley pattern, which is dendritic. Because of the change in pattern of both rivers and roads, the junction between the Ridge and Valley and Plateau provinces is very clear on a road map.

The altitude of the land is, in general, higher than that in the adjoining provinces—in places, dramatically so. The Catskills in New York State and the Allegheny Front in Pennsylvania form notable escarpments, standing well above the neighboring Ridge and Valley area.

Rock layers are essentially horizontal, as can be noted readily wherever they are visible on steep slopes. From a regional point of view, however, the Plateau has a broad, basin type of structure, which leads to the production of outward-facing cuesta scarps on the borders.

At the extreme north, the Plateau layers have a regional dip southward, away from the Adirondack Mountains and the shield area of Canada. The Mohawk River—Lake Ontario lowland trends east-west and has been cut into softer Plateau layers which lie between the hard crystalline rocks to the north and the more resistant, overlying Devonian layers which form the Plateau highlands extending from the Catskills and Helderbergs on the east through central New York State.

The highest parts of the province are found in the Catskill Mountains. A dramatic cuesta scarp, over 3,000 feet high in places, overlooks the Hudson River lowland. From the air, this scarp shows rounded and subdued, but very obvious, cliff-and-bench topography, a characteristic of plateau structure. The lowland to the east, at the foot of the scarp, has a definite northeast-southwest trend of small ridges and lowlands, appropriate to the Ridge and Valley province in which it lies. (See Raisz Structure, Section 5.)

Swift streams flow down the sides of the scarp and have cut deep gorges, such as that of the Kaaterskill Creek. On top, the Catskills are characterized by rolling topography, rounded mountain tops, and relatively narrow valleys.

South
APP. PLATEAU   LAKE PLAIN
Finger Lakes   Terrace

Watkins Glen   Penn Yan   Geneva   Barge Canal

Seneca L.   Waterloo   Clyde   Sod Ba

2,100   Ovid

Cayuga L.   Auburn

Owasso L.

Ithaca   Skaneateles L.   Drumlins

Oswego R.   Fulton

Catskill   —D—E—V—O—N—I—A—N—

Onondaga

Helderberg   Cayuga   SILURIAN   Niagara   Clinton   Utica   ORDOVIC

PALEOZOIC S

APPALACHIAN PLATEAU, FINGER LAKES—LAKE ONTARIO—CANADA.

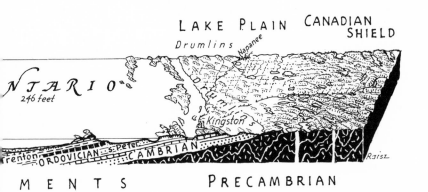

LAKE PLAIN · CANADIAN SHIELD · Drumlins · Napanee · ONTARIO · 246 feet · Kingston · Trenton · ORDOVICIAN · S. Peter · CAMBRIAN · Raisz · MENTS · PRECAMBRIAN

Opposite:
CATSKILL MOUNTAINS FROM THE EAST. The lowland in the foreground is part of the Ridge and Valley province. Note the faint development of cliffs and benches on the scarp face, indicating plateau structure. (Aero Service Division—Litton Industries)

The northern parts of the Plateau area, which have been glaciated, extend from central New York State into northern Pennsylvania and northeastern Ohio. The north-south-trending Finger Lakes of central New York State lie in glacially scoured valleys. They have very steep side walls and deeply eroded floors. The bottoms of lakes Seneca and Cayuga extend below sea level. Postglacial streams descend the sides of the valleys, and falls and rapids are found in a number of places. A number of relatively small but steep-walled valleys are cut into the glacially oversteepened valley sides, such as at Watkins Glen at the south end of Lake Seneca. Here, a prominent set of vertical north-south joints has markedly controlled the configuration of the eroded cliff faces.

In addition to the Finger Lakes, there are a large number of north-south-trending glaciated valleys which have been partially filled in with alluvium after the ice left, so that now they show wide, very flat floors rather than the classic U-shaped cross profile of the typical glaciated valley. The junction between the flat floor and the steep hillside is quite noticeable, often marking the contact between tilled fields and pasturage or hay fields, with wooded slopes higher still. In many places kames and kame terraces adorn the floors of the valleys, and till mantles the hills and slopes.

South of the area covered by ice, the structure and topography are basically the same, but the very obvious glacial features are lacking. In Pennsylvania, the east-facing scarp of the Allegheny Front is very prominent. (See Raisz Structure, Section 3.) To the west, inside the Plateau province, Laurel Hill and Chestnut Ridge are homoclinal ridges in the otherwise generally horizontal layers, and in the Cumberland Plateau section of Tennessee, Sequatchie Valley is an excellent example of an anticlinal structure. (See Raisz Structure, Section 6.)

The results of extensive strip mining for coal can be clearly seen from the air in West Virginia and Kentucky. Benches formed in the process of such mining appear like newly cut roads encircling hill tops. They were formed when the essentially horizontal coal layers were followed for a distance into the hill from their original position of outcrop.

7 | New England

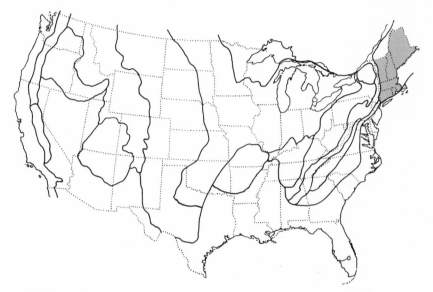

Geologically, this province is a continuation of the Appalachian Mountains from further south. Counterparts of the Ridge and Valley, Blue Ridge, and Piedmont provinces are found. The major differences in topography lie in the fact that all New England was covered by ice; thus, the most notable landscape features here are glacier-fashioned, either by erosion or by deposition.

Metamorphic and igneous rocks dominate. Granite, marble, and slate have been quarried extensively, and sand and gravel are dug from various glacial deposits, such as kames, eskers, and lake deltas. Terraces on the sides of a number of stream valleys mark former flood-plain levels, now in the process of being removed by the renewed cutting action of the present rivers.

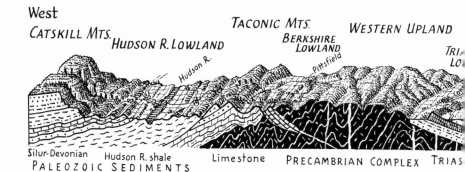

West

CATSKILL MTS. HUDSON R. LOWLAND   TACONIC MTS. BERKSHIRE LOWLAND   WESTERN UPLAND   TRI... LO...

Silur-Devonian   Hudson R. shale   Limestone   PRECAMBRIAN COMPLEX   TRIAS
PALEOZOIC SEDIMENTS

NEW ENGLAND, CATSKILL MOUNTAINS—BOSTON.

Lowlands are cut into softer sedimentary rock, such as the Connecticut River lowland and the Boston, Narragansett, and Norfolk basins.

Because of the hilly, rocky nature of the land, the cover of glacial debris is apt to be discontinuous, and ledges of metamorphic and igneous rocks frequently protrude. The glacial deposits are characteristically sandy and rocky in nature, thus reflecting the rocky bedrock over which the ice came, and from which it derived its load. The deposits associated with the glacier consist of ground moraine, including many erratics; drumlins; terminal moraines; and a great deal of material deposited by glacial meltwaters. The floors of drained glacial lakes give flat country. Delta deposits built into the vanished lakes are found at a slightly higher level. Kames, kame terraces, and eskers, all associated with stagnating ice, are plentiful, often being found in swampy, low-lying land marking the places where masses of ice lasted the longest.

In the western part of New England, the Taconic Mountains and the Berkshire Hills are counterparts of the Ridge and Valley region from further south. They resemble them in having rocks of the same age, which also were folded and eroded into resistant rock ridges and softer rock valleys. Here, however, the ridge and valley arrangement is not as obvious, and furthermore, the even elevation of the ridge tops, so notable further south, is not evident. In New England, the sedimentary rocks have been metamorphosed into slates, schist, phyllites, and marbles.

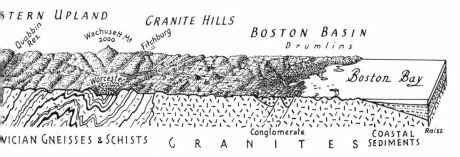

STERN UPLAND GRANITE HILLS BOSTON BASIN

Quabbin Res. Wachusett Mt 2000 Fitchburg Drumlins

Worcester Boston Bay

VICIAN GNEISSES & SCHISTS G R A N I T E S Conglomerate COASTAL SEDIMENTS Raise

A north-south valley in Vermont separates the Taconics from the Green Mountains. It is floored with relatively soft sediments, largely limestone, and is the New England equivalent of the Great Valley.

The Green Mountains, which can be considered the New England equivalent of the Blue Ridge province, form a maturely dissected range with rounded peaks which average about 2,000 feet in elevation. Mount Mansfield in Vermont is the highest elevation, somewhat over 4,000 feet. The range is about 20 miles wide at the Canadian border and 35 miles wide at the Massachusetts border.

East of the Green Mountains, the major part of New England is an area composed of generally low hills and valleys with swamps and lakes. Here and there a prominent peak rises as an erosional remnant (monadnock) above the general level of the low hills. Mount Wachusett and the Blue Hills in Massachusetts, Mount Monadnock (the type example) in southern New Hampshire, and further north, the large mass of the White Mountains and Mount Katahdin are all such isolated peaks.

The White Mountains in northern New Hampshire and the neighboring parts of Maine form the most rugged section of the province. Mount Washington, 6,288 feet above sea level, marks the highest elevation. This mountain and its attendant peaks in the Presidential Range extend above tree line and show rounded, boulder-strewn summits from the flanks of which cirque bites have been taken by glaciers. High, moderately flat areas, locally called lawns, lie somewhat below the actual summits of the peaks and may mark an old erosion surface, now uplifted well above sea level. Bedrock does not appear at the summit of Mount Washington, which is covered by an enormous pile of angular boulders, the result of intense postglacial frost wedging. Stone stripes on the lawns also indicate the continued importance of freeze-and-thaw cycles in moving and sorting materials.

Cirques are well developed on the flanks of Mount Washington and neighboring peaks. Such features as the Great Gulf, Tuckerman, Huntington, and King ravines are superb examples. Also in this part of New Hampshire, a number of classic U-shaped valleys have been carved out by the action of tongues of ice as they oozed through preglacial stream valleys. The "notches," or passes, such as Crawford, Franconia, Pinkham, and Dixville are examples.

The landscape features along the coast have resulted from the drowning of a glaciated and stream-carved land. Evidence of recent drowning, during the last 10,000 to 12,000 years, is shown by the presence of many estuaries and islands all along the coast. A notable collection of estuaries extending well inland and promontories and island groups pointing seaward is found along the coast of Maine. The structure of the rocks here trends roughly north-south; thus, the alignment of island groups and estuaries has this same trend.

Wave erosion and current action along the coast of Maine have encountered relatively resistant rocks; consequently, the results of their action are not very obvious. Small cliffs facing the open ocean and small discontinuous beaches are all that are found. Farther south in New Hampshire and along the Massachusetts coast, however, the seas encountered materials of less resistance, composed of extensive deposits of glacial material,

COAST OF MAINE, CASCO BAY AREA. (Photo by Laurence Lowry)

drumlins, and moraines. Thus, sand beaches and sea cliffs cut into the softer glacial debris are common. In Boston Harbor, the many drowned drumlins show cliffed edges on their seaward margins.

Nantasket Beach on the south side of Boston Harbor is a tombolo, which has joined a number of drumlin islands to the mainland. It is matched on the north side of Boston Bay by Lynn Beach, also a tombolo which has joined, in this case, rocky islets to the mainland.

The obvious presence of sea cliffs and beaches continues southward along the Rhode Island and Connecticut shores. Here also, glacial debris has formed a prolific and easily moved supply of material. Terminal moraines are notable on Cape Cod, Nantucket, and Martha's Vineyard.

The Connecticut River lowland is a region of deep red, Triassic sediments—shales and sandstone—with interbedded black basalt flows and intruded sills. This region extends from just south of the northern border of Massachusetts to Long Island Sound at New Haven. It is followed for the most part by the Connecticut River which leaves the lowland at Middletown, Connecticut, to follow a southeastward course across crystalline rocks to the sea at Old Lyme.

The whole group of Triassic rocks has been tilted toward the east along border faults, which has allowed these sediments to be dropped downward into the general level of the upland crystalline terrain. Since the dip is eastward, scarp faces of the more resistant flows and sills face westward, producing such features as the Hanging Hills at Meriden, East and West rocks at New Haven, and Mount Tom and the Holyoke ranges in Massachusetts.

In places, in addition to the basalt, some of the sedimentary layers, such as sandstone and conglomerate, are comparatively resistant and stand out as hills and ridges. Mount Sugarloaf, near Deerfield, Massachusetts, is such a hill.

8 | Adirondacks

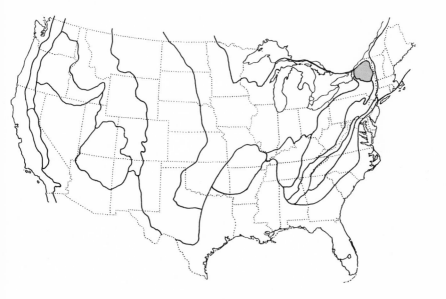

The Adirondack Mountains cover an area of about 10,000 square miles, roughly circular in shape. Rocks are igneous and metamorphic, Precambrian in age. In general, the higher parts are underlain by granite, and the lower by more easily eroded metamorphic rocks, often marble.

The general level of the province rises gently from the west to the higher eastern parts, where sixteen peaks exceed 4,000 feet in elevation. Mount Marcy, the highest, is 5,344 feet high. The western section is an area of relatively low relief, generally a few hundred feet at most, with many glacially rounded rock knobs.

Throughout the whole area, there are many lakes and swamps

LAKE PLACID, ADIRONDACK MOUNTAINS, NEW YORK. Note its rectangular shape. (Aero Service Division—Litton Industries)

with a network of rivers. In the east especially, this series of water features lies in a setting of steep wooded slopes, scarred here and there by landslides. The many lake basins (over 2,000) either were scoured out of bedrock by glacial erosion or are due to the damming up of preglacial stream valleys by glacial deposits. Many elongated lakes follow lowland areas, which are fault controlled. Terminal moraines are poorly developed, but glacial meltwater deposits are plentiful. There are flat, former lake floors, now drained; deltas built into now-vanished lakes; terraces along sides of valleys; and a remarkable series of eskers running northeast-southwest across the center of the area.

The region as a whole is drained by a roughly radial pattern of rivers which flow away from the higher central areas. However, a more detailed inspection shows a well-developed rectangular arrangement to the stream valleys and hills. Valleys, lakes, and ridges show a northeast-southwest trend, which is especially well developed in the more mountainous areas and is largely due to a series of faults which trends in this direction. A less evident "grain" in the landforms is present at right angles to this major trend; thus, a rectangular pattern can be detected. For instance, Lake Placid has a rectangular shape, the major dimensions lying northeast-southwest.

9 | *Interior Low Plateaus*

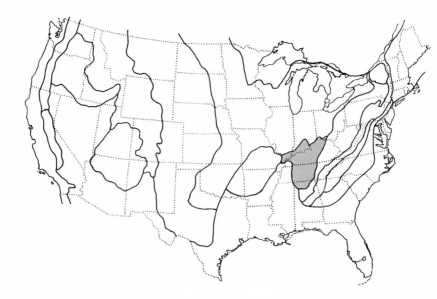

The rocks and general structure here are similar to that of the Appalachian Plateau, but the altitudes are somewhat lower and the relief is less. On the west, the deep reentrant of the Coastal Plain borders the province, and on the north there is a gradational boundary where rocks of similar age and general structure in the Central Lowlands have been glaciated. Much of the bedrock is thus obscured.

Topography is closely related to the type and arrangement of the rock layers. The general horizontal plateau structure is modified by the Cincinnati Arch. This is a low dome which trends nearly north-south. In detail, there are two major elevations, one centered at Lexington, Kentucky, in the Bluegrass region, and one at Nashville, Tennessee. Erosion of these domal structures has characteristically led to the formation of a series of cuestas surrounding them. The steep scarps face inward toward the center of the dome, and the gentle dip slope outward. In many places the scarp, instead of being an obvious cliff, consists of a zone of deeply eroded land, of deep reentrants and promontories, often with erosional remnants or outliers forming knobs in front. The cuestas from the scarp side often look far more like a row of hills than an extensive cliff face.

There are three major cuestas in the province: the Highland Rim around the Nashville Dome, Muldroughs Hills (Knobstone) escarpment around the southern parts of the Lexington area, and in the western areas of the province, a major cuesta called the Dripping Springs Escarpment in Kentucky and the Chester Escarpment in Indiana. The important resistant layers which form the cuestas are sandstone and chert-rich layers of limestone.

The dips of the layers on the flanks of the domes are moderate, with values usually less than 30 feet per mile. At any one outcrop, the layers with such a slight dip would appear to be horizontal, and only when followed some distance can a change in elevation of a given layer be noted.

The structural dome at Nashville has been eroded into what is topographically a basin, the Nashville Basin, which is bounded by the in-facing scarp of the Highland Rim. The area of the basin is roughly 60 by 100 miles, and the center is approximately 400 to 600 feet lower than the cuesta rim. The scarp has an irregular front, and the erosional outliers, or knobs, stand 200 to 400 feet above the basin floor. In shape, they range from conical to small, flat-topped hills, capped by sandstone with weaker shale underneath. At one time they were obviously parts of the cuesta, but are now isolated as a result of the retreat of the scarp by erosion.

In a number of places, limestone is bare of soil and is weath-

INTERIOR LOW PLATEAUS, TENNESSEE RIVER—NASHVILLE—BLUE RIDGE.

ered into a rough, corrugated, and furrowed surface called lapiés. Although such limestone areas, when moderately flat, may have a thin soil which can support the growth of some trees, they are often treeless. In the Nashville area, such areas are called barrens; elsewhere in the province, glades.

The Bluegrass area of Lexington, Kentucky, is structurally similar to the Nashville Basin, but erosion has not resulted in a similar topographic basin. It is a region of rolling lowlands developed on limestone and shale. There are some karst features in the limestone, but they are not well developed. Cuesta scarps are noticeable on the east, south, and southwest sides, and knobs are well developed on the east and south sides.

The rest of the province shows many diverse features, chief among which are irregular scarps, well-developed karst in places, and incised meanders. The Kentucky, Green, and Cumberland rivers all have excellent examples of incised meanders with well-developed slip-off and undercut slopes.

In limestone areas, surface streams are rare; consequently,

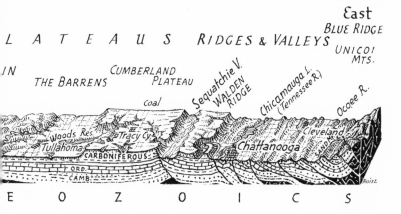

water takes an underground path to a large extent. The karst plain south of the Dripping Springs Escarpment, in the area northeast of Bowling Green, Kentucky, is an area of thousands of sinkholes and of many disappearing streams. Caves and the accompanying display of various dripstone deposits are common. Mammoth Cave, Kentucky, lies in this section.

10 | Central Lowlands

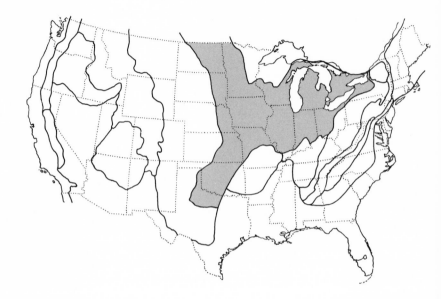

From southern Canada, where this province abuts against the Canadian Shield, to the Coastal Plain and from the Appalachian Plateau on the east to the Great Plains on the west, this area is bounded on most sides by higher land. Altitudes generally range from only a few hundred feet above sea level in the east to nearly 2,000 feet along the Great Plains border, and the relief is measured in tens to a few hundreds of feet at most. Some of the area is very flat, but most of it is gently rolling. Rock layers where seen in road or river cuts are horizontal, but do have regional dips associated with various broad warps. Dipping layers associated with the Cincinnati and Ozark domes extend into this province. Down-warped structures are represented by the Michigan and Illinois basins, which are features many miles across. Erosion of the gently dipping layers connected with these structures has led to the formation of extensive cuestas which may be followed for tens to hundreds of miles across the country.

Stream patterns characteristically are dendritic, and most rivers have gentle gradients, many of the major streams meandering across flood plains.

The generally horizontal structure is similar to that of the Great Plains province, but the types of scenery are sufficiently different to merit dividing these provinces. The division is based on a combination of age of rock, topography, and elevation. Along much of the boundary, especially in North Dakota and at the south in Texas, a distinct east-facing scarp marks the eastern edge of the Great Plains. Between these areas the line is gradational and thus arbitrary in places. The Great Plains rise westward; near the Rockies they reach an elevation of a mile or more. In the Great Plains the rainfall is generally less than 20 inches per year, whereas it is more than this in the Central Lowlands. Such a difference in rainfall results in semi-aridity in the Plains, permitting grass to grow on the uplands, but trees only in the valleys along the river banks. This tree cover becomes increasingly extensive in the Lowlands. The bedrock of the Lowlands is Paleozoic in age, whereas in the Plains it is Mesozoic to Cenozoic.

The imprint of continental glaciers in the northern parts of the Interior Lowlands is marked. Lakes and swamps, moraines, and outwash deposits are all common. The present courses of the rivers have been largely determined by glacial action. The Missouri, Ohio, Mississippi, and Wabash rivers, for example, follow paths markedly different from those formed before the time of the great continental glacier. The glacier often filled preglacial valleys; when the ice left, the rivers that developed found other paths as they flowed among the recently dumped debris.

CENTRAL LOWLANDS, GREEN BAY—TORONTO.

The preglacial topography, which is now in large part "drowned" in glacial debris, resembles that which developed in the Interior Low Plateaus; that is, it was a region of domes and basins, each with encircling cuestas. Now only the highest cuestas protrude through the glacial cover, such as the Niagara Cuesta. This scarp, over which the Niagara River drops at Niagara Falls, can be followed for many miles through Ontario and New York State.

Although moraines and other glacial deposits have a moderate relief, the major effect of the glaciers has been to lessen the preglacial relief of the land by filling in many preglacial valleys. However, the influence of the preglacial topography on the location and shape of the moraines is marked. Lowlands, such as Green Bay, Lake Michigan, Saginaw Bay, and Lake Erie, afforded passageways for the advance of the ice, which flowed as lobes, southward down them. End moraines associated with the front of the ice tongues are therefore looped, each loop being associated with a lowland. This explains the

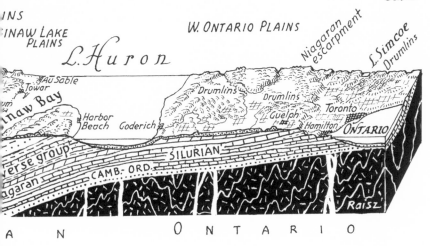

lobate and interlobate nature of the extensive development of terminal and recessional moraines here.

The bulk of the material deposited by any glacier is not carried far from its source, perhaps a mile or so. Such a derivation of material from the local bedrock explains why till deposits vary so much from place to place. Where bedrock is composed of resistant metamorphic and igneous rocks, such as in the Lake Superior Upland, the Adirondacks, and New England, boulders and coarse deposits of sand and gravel are found in the drift, whereas in areas of more easily broken sedimentary materials, such as shale, sandstone, and limestone, as found in many parts of the Lowland province, the deposits are much finer, often containing much clay.

During approximately the last 1,000,000 years, there have been four times of ice advance over the northern parts of the Central Lowlands. Drift of each of these advances can be identified. The oldest (Nebraskan) is found only underneath the surface; that is, more recent advances with associated drift sheets extended farther southward than did the Nebraskan ice. The Wisconsin, the most recent advance, did not extend as far south as the middle two advances, the Kansan and Illinoisian. The different ages of drift have given two generally different types of topography; that of the young drift, Wisconsin in age, characterized by lakes and swamps, moraines, drumlins, eskers, and kames, and that of the older drift, which lacks these features because enough time has elapsed for their destruction.

When they are viewed from the air, the areas of young drift seem peppered with sheets of shining water. These lake basins are of various origins. Many are kettle holes, some are the result

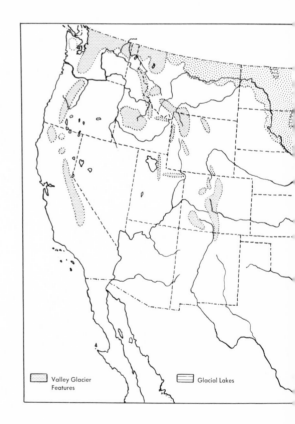

Valley Glacier Features   Glacial Lakes

of the damming up of rivers by glacial dump, and some have been carved out of bedrock.

An especially fine field of drumlins is found near Fond du Lac at the South end of Lake Winnebago in Wisconsin. Other major drumlin fields are found in northern Michigan and in New York State, just south of Lake Ontario.

Interlobate moraines are developed where two lobes intersect; they are thus oriented with a long axis parallel to the general

AREAS OF GLACIAL FEATURES IN THE UNITED STATES

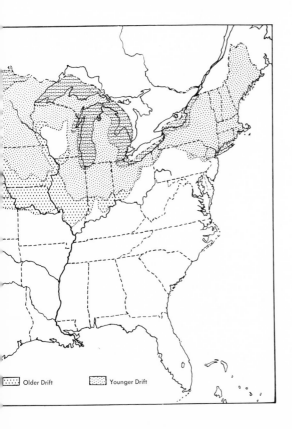

advance of the ice, since they developed on the sides of ice tongues. Kettle Moraine in Wisconsin is an excellent example. About 120 miles long, it was built by the coalescence of the Green Bay and Lake Michigan lobes. This moraine, which trends slightly east of north, has associated with it some excellent examples of glacio-fluviatile deposits, such as eskers, kames, and kettle holes.

The Great Lakes are, of course, the most notable landscape features in the section of young drift. Their origin is intimately tied in with the presence and activity of the continental glaciers. They now lie in what was formerly a series of lowland areas cut out by streams. These preglacial valleys were deepened by glacial action, and there was also some warping of the crust under the ice load, a warping which is still present to some extent. The floors of all the lakes, except Lake Erie, now extend below sea level. Their present extent and shapes are not as they were during the various times of glacial advance and retreat. This is shown by the presence of exposed lake floor, such as that around Detroit and Chicago. Furthermore, raised beaches and wave-cut cliffs can be noted at various places, all attesting to the former greater extent of these bodies of water.

The continental glacier provided an enormous supply of meltwater which had to flow southward away from the ice. Such water took a number of paths, which now show evidence of having been major sluiceways. Present stretches along the Mississippi, Ohio, and Wabash rivers all indicate that at times in the past much more water flowed through them than now. Some of the debris carried southward is now found as sand and gravel terraces, which were left along the sides of the valleys as the rivers subsided. Sand dunes and extensive loess deposits on

WHITE RIVER, INDIANA. Note meanders, abandoned channels, and sand bars on the inside of the meander loops. (Photography— CSS–USDA)

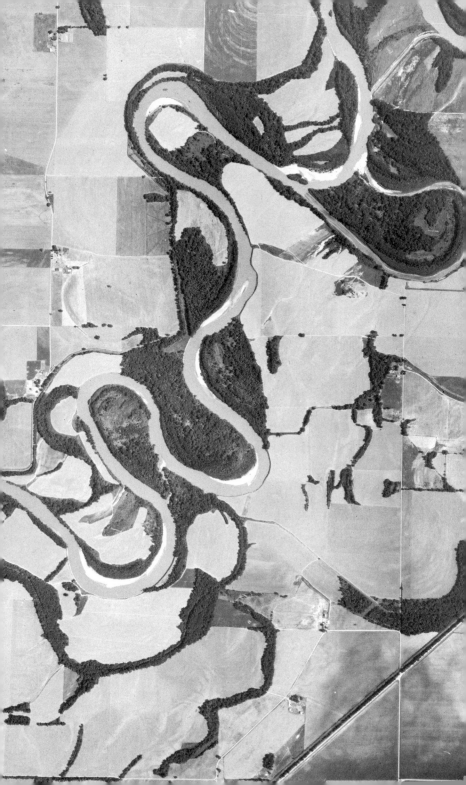

the upland areas near the sluiceways were produced when the wind blew the smaller loose material around after it was laid down by the rivers. Loess deposits, up to 100 feet thick in places, are found near some of the major routes taken by the meltwaters. The major characteristic of loess as a landform is its ability to stand up in vertical cliffs even when cut into by streams or roads.

Lake Agassiz, the largest ice-marginal lake in North America, existed in this region. The floor of part of this lake is now exposed, giving the flat country on the border between Minnesota and North Dakota. Northward, the lake widened out in Canada. The former presence of Lake Agassiz, indicated primarily by the flat floor of deposition, is also shown by many abandoned beach ridges which can be noted as one travels away from the lake floor before rising at last to the rolling country of drift on the sides of the lake.

The Wisconsin Driftless Area, lying mostly in the southeastern part of the state with minor extensions into the neighboring parts of Illinois, Iowa, and Minnesota, escaped being covered by ice. The usual topography associated with the former presence of an overriding mass of ice is missing. Layered, horizontal sedimentary rock is obvious, and delicate erosional remnants can be noted in many places. Any ice advance through here would have destroyed these features and have buried the bedrock under piles of debris, as it did in surrounding areas.

The reason for the presence of the Driftless Area here lies in the fact that it was protected by the Superior uplands, and the ice which was oozing southward was channeled down the Lake Superior lowland on one side and the Lake Michigan lowland on the other.

The areas of older drift, the till plains, are marked by a total absence of the usual features which are associated with the former presence of glaciers. The time since deposition by ice sheets has been long enough so that lakes and swamps have been filled in, and the original forms of typical glacial deposits have been destroyed by erosion. Many areas are gently rolling, and elsewhere the land may be flat over large distances, with a relief of less than 10 feet in a distance of 1 mile. Loess deposits are extensive as a thin covering over the till plains. In some areas, especially in southern Iowa, the till has been so well dissected by a well-integrated system of streams that the original glacial surfaces are entirely lacking.

Most rivers here also follow paths different from their preglacial courses, which were clogged and often totally obliterated by glacial fill. Now, when such rivers cut down through the soft glacial material, they may find themselves constrained to flow on formerly buried, hard-rock ridges and upland country, except where they perchance follow for a short distance some preglacial valley which, filled as it is with soft glacial material, will be eroded more easily than the bedrock. Such a situation, for instance, explains the marked widening of the Wabash River in central Indiana near the junction of Miami and Wabash counties.

The Arbuckle and Wichita mountains are included in the lowland area. The Arbuckle uplift in south central Oklahoma consists of homoclinal ridges surrounding a granite core, which is deeply weathered and eroded, and shows a relief of less than 500 feet. In contrast, the Wichita Mountains in southwestern Oklahoma have a relief of 1,000 feet or more. They also have a granite core exposed by erosion.

11 | The Great Plains

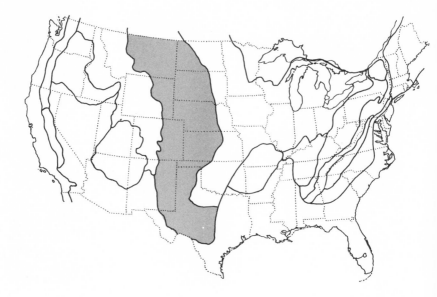

The Great Plains, in contrast with the Central Lowlands, are higher in elevation, have a greater relief, receive less rainfall, and are composed primarily of Mesozoic and Cenozoic sediments rather than Paleozoic. In general, the rainfall is less than 20 inches per year, compared with greater rainfall to the east. This results in short, rather than tall, grasses to the east and the presence of trees only in valleys along rivers. Very approximately, the 100th Meridian marks the boundary between these two provinces.

The sedimentary layers are essentially horizontal throughout, with broad regional dips associated with basins and domes. This structure leads, on erosion, to the production of cuestas.

The general elevation of the land decreases from about a mile near the Rocky Mountains to somewhat less than 2,000 feet at the boundary with the Central Lowlands. Some areas are very flat, with long stretches of monotonous country, whereas others may have quite a bit of relief, such as the deeply eroded areas along cuesta scarps. Badlands topography may develop along rivers bluffs, where erosion is rapid and fine-grained sediments outcrop. Glacial deposits and sand dunes have, in places, given the land a moderate relief. Some areas, such as the Black Hills and various other outliers of the Rocky Mountains, are rugged and are included in the Plains because they are entirely surrounded by flat country.

The western boundary of the Plains is clear and abrupt throughout most of the province, where the Rocky Mountains rise some thousands of feet along a moderately straight front. This is especially notable in Colorado, where the Front Range rises from the Colorado Piedmont. (See Raisz Structure, Section 9.) Only where the plains abut against the Wyoming Basin section of the Rocky Mountains is there lacking a clear-cut topographic boundary between these two provinces. Many parts of the Wyoming Basin resemble the Great Plains country.

The eastern boundary is marked at the north by the Missouri Escarpment, which is a rise in land of about 500 feet from the elevation of the Central Lowlands. At the south the junction of the Great Plains with the Coastal Plain is marked by the Balcones Escarpment, and the junction with the Interior Lowlands by the Caprock Escarpment. Both of these scarps are extensive and notable erosional features. The eastern boundary of the province in Kansas and Nebraska is less well marked.

The province as a whole can be divided into a number of sections, each having its own characteristic modifications of the basic underlying horizontal structure.

North of the Missouri River, in northern Montana and northwestern North Dakota, the region has been glaciated, showing typical glacial features: lakes, swamps, moraines, and various meltwater deposits. The boundary of this part with the Central Lowlands is marked by the east-facing Missouri Escarpment, topped with a series of end moraines, the so-called Coteau du Missouri. The total relief is in the order of a few hundreds of feet in a typical morainal topography. The former presence of ice-marginal lakes is indicated by flat, drained lake floors, such as that southwest of Great Falls, Montana.

The unglaciated sections of the Great Plains extend from central Montana to the Coastal Plain in Texas. The more deeply eroded parts of this large area lie along the edges, and the least eroded part is at the center, in the High Plains area.

From the Missouri River southward to roughly the South Dakota–Nebraska line, where the north-facing Pine Ridge Escarpment marks the beginning of the High Plains section, there is much greater evidence of erosion than is shown further south. A number of rivers and their tributary systems have cut moderately deep valleys into the otherwise generally flat country. The development of extensive areas of badlands topography is especially well shown between the White and Cheyenne rivers, east of the Black Hills, and also along the Little Missouri River in southwestern North Dakota.

In Montana, there are two types of isolated outliers of the Rocky Mountains. Some are domal uplifts which show an exposed Precambrian core of resistant igneous or metamorphic rocks with surrounding hogbacks. Examples are the Big Belt, Little Belt, Little Rockies, and Big Snowy mountains. Another type of outlier results from mid-Tertiary intrusions and extrusions. Dikes, sills, and flows can all be seen. Examples are Highwood, Judith, Crazy, Bearpaw and Castle mountains, and the Sweetgrass Hills.

The Black Hills in western South Dakota compose the largest and most important of the Rocky Mountain outliers. It is a north-south-trending dome, with steeper dips on the east than on the west. There is a Precambrian core of granite which forms the highest parts of the Hills. Harney Peak has an elevation of 7,242 feet, which is about 4,000 feet higher than the surrounding plains. Hogback ridges surround the central core. There is an outer, very noticeable, ridge of sandstone and an inner one of limestone. Between these ridges lies the impressive Red Valley, cut into red sediments. The limestone, because of the asymmetry of the dome, forms a cuesta on the west and a hogback on the east.

A number of small volcanic intrusions form peaks in the northern parts of the Black Hills area, such as Bear Butte on the northeast, Devil's Tower on the northwest, and many others in between.

The High Plains extend from Nebraska into Texas. They are the flattest and least-eroded section of the Great Plains and have, in general, a depositional rather than erosional surface. They are composed of remnants of a broad apron of sediments laid down in the Tertiary by streams flowing from the Rockies and originally extending for hundreds of miles away from the mountains. At the present time, a few widely spaced streams have cut broad, flat-floored valleys. The valley walls are characteristically cut by gullies and side tributaries, so that on leaving the valley, a zone of dissected land must be traversed before reaching the flat, extensive interstream uplands. A notable, wide valley is that of the Platte River at Goshen Hole on the border between Wyoming and Nebraska.

In Nebraska, there is an area of about 24,000 square miles where sand dunes dominate the scene. Here, there are many interdune ephemeral lakes, which have no surface outlets, the water disappearing by evaporation or seepage underground. The sand composing the dunes has come from the weathering of a sandy formation, the Ogallala. Outside the area of dunes, there are extensive loess deposits.

The Ogallala formation, which outcrops over much of the

High Plains, is found from South Dakota southward through the Texas Panhandle. In the Texas areas, the topmost part of this formation is resistant to erosion owing to calcium carbonate cement, forming the Caprock Escarpment.

Many shallow depressions, ranging in size from less than 1 foot deep and 10 or so feet in diameter to tens of feet deep and miles across, are found distributed throughout the High Plains. The origin of such depressions is not clear in all cases. Many probably are deflation hollows; some could be the result of differential compaction of the unconsolidated materials under the surface; some have been explained by the solution of soluble layers; and some are perhaps the result of buffalo wallows, where the land is stirred up and the wind blows the loosened particles of sand and dust away. These depressions are apt to remain for a long time in such a flat terrain because the removal of surface material by rain wash and running water is very slow down the gentle slopes which prevail there. Such shallow, closed depressions have, of course, no outlet at the surface, and in the drier parts of the region, they may be the location of salinas (salt deposits), as are common in the Llano Estacado of Texas.

The Edwards Plateau of west Texas represents a continuation of the same general type of flat land found in the Llano Estacado. The Tertiary cover of the High Plains, however, has been removed, exposing a layer of Cretaceous limestone which, on erosion, has resulted in many sinkholes, underground rivers, caverns, and springs.

The Tertiary wedge of sediments which has been preserved in the High Plains has been extensively eroded both along the eastern and western borders of the province. In Colorado, this eroded section is bordered on the west by a zone of upturned

GREAT PLAINS, SOUTH DAKOTA. The region shown here is southeast of Pierre. The land is divided into mile-square sections. (Aero Service Division—Litton Industries)

sedimentary rocks. The resistant layers form a striking series of hogbacks which parallel the front of the Rocky Mountains for many miles. At the Garden of the Gods near Colorado Springs, the sediments are vertical. Between the hogbacks everywhere, there are longitudinal valleys which parallel the ridges. Near Boulder, Colorado, a resistant sandstone layer lies directly on granite, and erosion has formed a series of flatiron-shaped remnants leaning up against the mountain front.

The dip of the rock layers rapidly decreases eastward and soon becomes horizontal. The elevation of the land surface drops from a mile above sea level near the mountains to 4,000 feet in eastern Colorado, where the High Plains rise slightly above the piedmont area.

In southern Colorado and northern New Mexico, lava flows, sills, and dikes are locally important. Lava-capped mesas are typical forms here. The Spanish Peaks are eroded small masses of granite with many radiating dikes.

At the southwest edge of the Great Plains in New Mexico, there is a broad depression drained by the Pecos River. In this area, which lies between the High Plains and the mountains of the Basin and Range province, there are some very soluble rocks, such as limestone, halite, and anhydrite. Erosion of these has resulted in many caves, such as Carlsbad, sinkholes, and disappearing streams.

On the east side of the High Plains, there are two areas which show extensive erosion. One lies in west central Kansas, and the other is in central Texas. In the latter area, the Central Mineral district of Texas, a broad domal structure has been eroded to expose a Precambrian core of igneous and metamorphic rocks, and in-facing cuesta scarps are found surrounding the structure.

12 | Interior Highlands

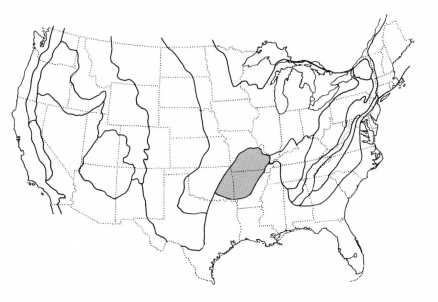

The Interior Highlands are composed of the Ozark Plateaus at the north and the folded Ouachita Mountains at the south. The Ozarks are carved from a broad asymmetric dome where the maximum elevation occurred near the eastern edge. The structure covers about 40,000 square miles and resembles, in basic form, the Nashville Dome. Here, however, there is no analogous topographic basin at the center, but instead a core of Precambrian igneous rocks, the Saint François Mountains, which stands high because of its resistance to weathering and erosion. The dips of the sediments away from these mountains are 70 to 80 feet per mile toward the east and only 10 to 20 feet per mile toward the west. The dips to the north and to the south are between these two values.

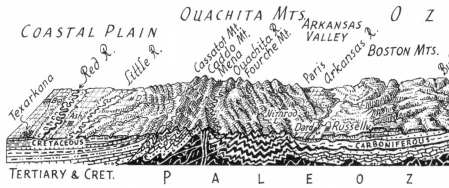

SSW

COASTAL PLAIN

OUACHITA MTS.

ARKANSAS VALLEY

O Z

Texarkana   Red R.   Little R.   Cassatot Mt.   Caddo Mt.   Mena   Ouachita R.   Fourche Mt.   Paris   Arkansas R.   BOSTON MTS.

Wimrod   Dardr   Russellv

CRETACEOUS

CARBONIFEROUS

TERTIARY & CRET.   P   A   L   E   O   Z

INTERIOR HIGHLANDS, TEXARKANA–SAINT LOUIS.

There are four major divisions in the Ozark region: The Saint François Mountains, the Salem Plateau surrounding them, the Springfield Plateau on the north, west, and south, and the Boston Mountains on the south side. Limestone and dolomite are common in the plateaus, and sandstone and shale are predominant in the Boston Mountains. Chert, found in the limestones, is so prevalent that it frequently chokes stream channels and fills incipient sinkholes. A number of rivers have incised their meandering courses into the plateau uplands. Many caves have been dissolved out of the limestone in both the Springfield and Salem plateaus.

Rounded granite peaks are common in the Saint François Mountains. Streams have cut wide valleys where they flow on sediments but are constricted along those parts of their paths where they flow on igneous rocks. Thus in different stretches, the same stream may have a broad valley for part of the way and a narrow gorgelike appearance elsewhere.

Rocks of the Salem Plateau entirely encircle the Saint François Mountains. Cuestas with irregularly receding scarps are well developed, and interstream areas are broad and rela-

tively flat. Many large springs are present. Big Spring, Carter County, Missouri, is the largest, with an average daily flow of 252,000,000 gallons. It emerges from the base of a limestone cliff. The flow of springs in this area fluctuates quickly in response to local rainfall, thus showing the very effective underground system of passageways which must exist.

The Springfield Plateau is another limestone plateau, with scenery similar to that of the Salem Plateau, from which it is separated by the Eureka Springs, or Burlington Escarpment. There are fewer springs with smaller volumes than in the Salem Plateau.

The Boston Mountains form an east-west belt of rough country where dissection of the rocks is relatively greater than in the Springfield Plateau. The boundary with the latter is marked by a prominent north-facing escarpment capped by a resistant sandstone. On the south side of the Boston Mountains, the dip of the layers increases as the folded rocks of the Ouachita Mountains are approached.

The Ouachita Mountains are composed of strongly folded sedimentary rocks with an east-west trend. They lie parallel and to the south of the Boston Mountains, covering an area roughly 225 miles long east to west and 100 miles wide north to south. At the north side, the Arkansas Valley section is primarily a lowland region with less intensely folded rocks than at the south. Although much of the area here is lowland, there are a number of resistant layers outcropping which form hogback ridges rising prominently above the general level of the land. Structures similar to those in the Appalachian Ridge and Valley region are present, such as anticlinal, synclinal, and monoclinal ridges and valleys. A number of synclinal ridges are so broad that they resemble an elongated mesa. Many of the folds plunge; therefore, there are converging and diverging ridges and horseshoe bends.

South of the Arkansas Valley, the Ouachita Mountains have ridge crests which rise prominently above valleys, giving a relief of over 1,000 feet. Converging, diverging, and S-bend ridges and valleys are common.

13 | Superior Upland

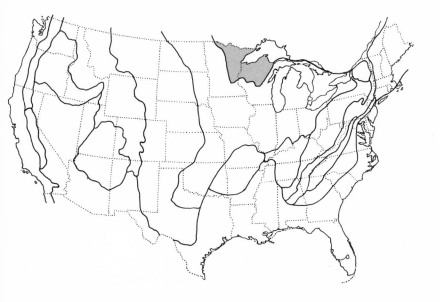

The Superior Upland is a relatively small extension into the United States of the enormous Precambrian Shield of Canada. In this respect it resembles the Adirondack Mountains.

The rocks are resistant, metamorphic, and igneous in nature, and the relief is moderate.

The most obvious landscape features of the whole area are those due to glaciation. At the north, where ice scour has been greatest, rock-basin lakes, rock striations, and *roches mouton-nées* are common. At the south, where there is a thicker pile of glacial drift, the bedrock has often been obscured, and lakes are found on and in glacial meltwater deposits. It is a land of

LAKES IN NORTHERN WISCONSIN. These are glacial lakes. (Photo by Wisconsin Natural Resources Department, Madison, Wisconsin)

lakes, swamps, and generally poor, slow drainage. The bedrock topography, where it is not covered by glacial debris, often shows an alignment of ridges and valleys, which reflect the structure of the metamorphosed sediments. Such an arrangement can be noted near the Canadian border, where there is a series of east-west monoclinal ridges and intervening valleys, the latter often containing a lake. In areas of intrusive igneous rocks, there is a more heterogeneous arrangement of landforms.

Lake Superior, the only Great Lake lying in this region, covers about 32,000 square miles, and the floor of the lake extends 700 feet below sea level. Such a depth is probably due to a combination of glacial scour, down-faulting, and incomplete rebound from the depression due to the thick ice load.

14 | Rocky Mountains

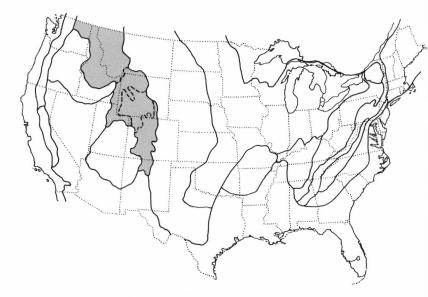

The Rocky Mountains form a rugged barrier which extends from northern New Mexico through the United States and Canada. They are composed of a number of separate ranges roughly parallel one to the other.

In the United States, the junction between the Rockies and the Great Plains is, for the most part, abrupt and striking. The mountains rise thousands of feet in a very few miles. Only at the Wyoming Basin section is this not so. Here, a Great Plains type of topography separates the southern group of mountains from the middle and northern groups. The Rockies are also markedly higher than their neighboring western provinces, the Columbia Plateau, the Basin and Range area, and the Colorado Plateau.

Granite and metamorphic rocks generally outcrop in the cores of the mountain ranges where uplift and the resulting erosion have been greatest. Sedimentary rocks are found on the flanks, or in down-faulted or down-folded areas. The resistant sediments form hogbacks where the dip is steep and cuestas where it is more gentle. Into the less resistant layers, valleys are cut.

Elevations are high, with many peaks over 14,000 feet, and relief is generally over a mile. Evergreen forests are present in most mountains. The streams are swift, rapids and waterfalls are common, and the divides between rivers are often sharp.

At the higher elevations, glacial scenery is beautifully developed. Cirques, arêtes, horns, U-shaped valleys, rock scratches and polish, and *roches moutonnées* all attest to the erosional activity of ice. End and lateral moraines and valleys partially filled with outwash material are evidence for glacial deposition. A few small glaciers, especially in the Northern Rockies, still persist.

Steep hillsides promote the development of many talus slopes, landslide scars, and mud flows. Everywhere there is evidence for the slipping and sliding and falling of rock debris downhill.

The Rocky Mountains can conveniently be divided, on the basis of structure, location, and types of landforms, into four parts: Southern Rockies (1), Wyoming Basin (2), Middle Rockies (3), and Northern Rockies (4).

SOUTHERN ROCKIES

The group of ranges comprising the Southern Rockies lies primarily in Colorado, with an extension into New Mexico, the Sangre de Cristo Mountains, and two projections into Wyoming, the Laramie Mountains on the east, and the Medicine Bow Mountains on the west.

The major ranges, which all trend north-south, are anticlinal in structure and are separated from each other by inter-

FRONT RANGE OF THE ROCKY MOUNTAINS, COLORADO. This view, looking north, shows hogback ridges which typically occur along the boundary with the Great Plains. (U.S. Geological Survey)

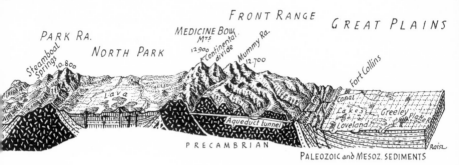

ROCKY MOUNTAINS, PARK RANGE—FRONT RANGE—GREAT PLAINS.

montane, down-folded or down-faulted basins. The most notable of these are North Park, Middle Park, South Park, Wet Mountain Valley, and San Luis Valley. The basins are floored by Tertiary sediments and some lava.

Erosion of the anticlinal mountains has exposed cores of Precambrian granite and metamorphic rocks, and monoclinal ridges and valleys on the flanks.

The highest elevations of the whole Rocky Mountain system are in Colorado. Some of the major peaks over 14,000 feet are Longs Peak (14,255), Pikes Peak (14,109), and Mount Evans (14,264).

The Colorado Front Range is a major landform, extending for 185 miles north to south. It rises very abruptly from the Great Plains, which is here about a mile above sea level. The abrupt rise of about 3,000 feet is followed by a more gradual rise of general elevation as one moves into the central part of the range. The minor peaks reach roughly to the same general elevation, perhaps a dissected peneplain, above which the major peaks, such as Pikes Peak and Longs Peak, rise in majestic grandeur.

The major north-south anticlinal structure of this range is, in detail, modified by some minor folding and cross faults. The latter have produced some offsetting of the hogback ridges in the foothill belt, such as that in the Loveland area.

The effects of valley glaciers are prominent on the higher peaks, as shown so well in Rocky Mountain National Park.

Flattop Mountain, slightly over 12,000 feet in elevation, has a remarkably level surface on top, which may represent, according to some geologists, a small remnant of an uplifted, former erosion surface or peneplain.

The Laramie Range continues the Front Range structure into Wyoming. The east limb of the anticline is somewhat steeper than the west, and thus the hogback ridges are steeper on this side. At the "Gangplank" in Wyoming, the Tertiary wedge of sediments, composed of material worn off the eroded mountains, has not been eroded as it has been farther south near the Front Range in the Colorado Piedmont. Thus it is possible to travel up a gentle slope from the Great Plains onto Precambrian granite of the mountains. The erosion surface here, called the Sherman Peneplain, is an undulating one with a thick cover of weathered granite debris.

The San Juan Mountains are composed chiefly of Tertiary volcanic rocks; thus they are unlike most of the ranges in the Southern Rockies in composition and structure. Excellent glacial scenery is found here and very active mass-wasting is evident. The classic example of a mud flow, the "Slumgullion" flow, dammed up a branch of the Gunnison River to form Lake San Cristobal.

Volcanic features are found at a number of places in the Southern Rockies. One very striking feature is the Valles Caldera on the west flank of the Jemez Mountains. The floor of this is about 15 miles in diameter and has been arched upward, thus indicating activity after the formation of the caldera itself. Many cones can be found on the margin.

The intermontane basins form major lowland areas which separate the ranges. North and Middle Parks together form a north-south basin 100 by 40 miles. It is separated into two parts by the Rabbit Ears Range. North Park is broad and flat-floored with a number of notable terraces on the sides. Middle Park has more relief due to a number of faults which cross it.

South Park is a basin approximately 35 by 45 miles in dimension. A number of small folds and faults cross the area. The elevation of the floor lies between 8,500 and 10,000 feet, the surrounding mountains rising still higher. Stream terraces, moraines, both lateral and terminal, and outwash plains are found.

The San Luis Valley lies between the Sangre de Cristo Mountains on the east and the San Juan Mountains on the west. It is about 50 miles wide and extends north-south as an intermontane basin structure for 150 miles. The floor of this remarkably flat valley is veneered with extensive stream deposits. A few volcanic hills rise prominently above the flats. A large alluvial fan, 20 miles in radius, has been built by the Rio Grande as it enters the valley near Del Norte.

WYOMING BASIN

The Wyoming Basin is an extension into the Rocky Mountain province of Great Plains' topography. It is reached from the Plains by a gap between the Laramie Range of the Southern Rockies and the Bighorn Mountains of the Middle Rockies.

The basin as a whole consists of a group of asymmetric basins separated one from another by uplifted anticlinal mountain structures, which continue the major trend of the Rocky Mountains across this province. These structures, however, have been largely buried under a thick covering of Tertiary sediments and now are in the process of being partially exhumed.

The Precambrian basement on which the later rocks are laid lies very deep under the basins, 4 to 5 miles below present seal level; in the major uplifts between the basins, it is well above sea level—in places, over 3 miles.

West

BIGHORN MOUNTAINS

BIGHORN BASIN

Bighorn R. Norwood R. Cuestas

Cloud Peak 13125

GREAT Flatirons

5680

OIL

Worland 4050 ft.

Buffalo 4850

Eocene N.W. Colo. JURA TR CARB DEVON DEVON CRET

CRETACEOUS   PALEOZOIC   G R A N I T E   EOCEN

ROCKY MOUNTAINS, BIGHORN MOUNTAINS.

The types of erosional landforms found in the basin areas are cuestas, hogbacks, badlands topography (for example, Hell's Half Acre, west of Casper), rock benches, stream terraces, mesas, buttes, and deflation hollows. Big Hollow in the Laramie Basin is one of the largest of such wind-formed hollows. It is 300 feet deep and covers an area 3 by 9 miles. Playa lakes are found in several areas, and sand dunes have been formed where there is an adequate supply of sand.

The Bridger (Green River) Basin has well-known shales containing beautifully preserved, carbonized fossil fish. These sediments were laid down in fresh-water lakes about 50,000,000 years ago.

The uplifted sections of the Wyoming Basin commonly have eroded cores of Precambrian granite and metamorphic rocks. Hogbacks and cuestas are found on the flanks.

The drainage in many places has apparently been superimposed onto more resistant rocks of the uplifts from a cover of sediments which is now being stripped away. Such a history explains the many water gaps cut by streams which take the more difficult route through and across areas of resistant rock where a slight detour would have taken them around such areas. Many examples of superposition are found in this and the neighboring areas of the Middle and Southern Rockies. The Sweetwater River, west of Alcova, Wyoming, has cut a gorge through a resistant ridge to form Devil's Gate. A shift in path of about half a mile would have allowed this river to avoid the ridge entirely. The Bighorn Canyon through the north end of the Bighorn Mountains, the Wind River Canyon through Owl Creek Mountains, and the cut made by the Laramie River across the Laramie Range are other classic examples of superposition.

MIDDLE ROCKIES

There is much diversity of structure and rock types in the Middle Rockies' section. Anticlinal mountains, fault-block mountains, and areas of volcanic rocks are all found here. They are lumped together, not because of similarity of landforms, but because they are geographic neighbors.

The anticlinal mountains—Bighorn, Wind River, Uinta, and Beartooth—are similar in structure and topography to the Southern Rockies. They all have exposed, eroded cores of Precambrian rocks—granite and metamorphics—with flanks of tilted sedimentary rocks.

The Bighorn Mountains provide a classic example of this type of anticlinal mountain range. The remnant of an uplifted erosion surface is shown by extensive high-level areas of very low relief. The crest of the range has a number of excellent cirques cut into it.

The Wind River Mountains form an isolated range trending northwest-southeast, about 125 miles long and 40 miles wide. The Wind River Basin lies on the northeast, and the Green River Basin on the southwest. There is an excellect display of mountain-type glacial features in the area.

The Uinta Mountains, unlike most ranges in the Rocky Mountain province, have an east-west trend. The anticlinal fold,

BEARTOOTH MOUNTAINS, MONTANA. Note the cirques cutting into the elevated peneplain. (Montana Highway Commission)

which is slightly overturned toward the north, is roughly 150 miles long and 30 to 40 miles wide. The highest peak (Kings Peak) is 13,500 feet in elevation, that is, about 8,500 feet higher than the floor of the Green River Basin to the north. There is a beautiful series of cirques cut into the main mountain ridge both from the north and the south. This gives a scalloped appearance to an otherwise smoothly rounded elongated mountain mass.

The Beartooth Mountains lie to the north of the Absarokas, mostly in Montana. The eastern front of the range rises abruptly, almost a mile, from the general level of the Great Plains. A high-level, subsummit peneplain 10,000 to 11,000 feet in elevation, is deeply incised by U-shaped valleys and cirques. On the southwest side of the range, there are many ice-scoured rock-basin lakes and *roches moutonnées,* which were formed by an ice cap which existed there.

The Bighorn Basin, between the Absaroka Mountains and the Bighorn Mountains, resembles the Great Plains and the basins of the Wyoming Basin area in both topography and geologic history. At one time it was much more deeply filled with alluvium than it is now. The more recent, partial excavation, following a general uplift of the whole Rocky Mountain area, has caused the superposition of a number of streams onto resistant rock ridges, hidden at one time. Such a history also explains the presence of remnants of stream deposits now found well above the present level of the basin floor.

The fault-block mountains of the Middle Rocky region— Grand Tetons, Wasatch, and a few other smaller ones—lie in the western part of the province.

The Grand Tetons consist of a block of the crust, 30 miles long north to south and 10 to 15 miles wide, which has been uplifted along a fault lying on the east margin. A dramatically abrupt rise of extensively glaciated peaks is seen from Jackson Hole on the east side. The highest peak, Grand Teton, is 13,800 feet in elevation and stands a mile and a half above the general level of the alluvial flats of the down-faulted Jackson Hole.

In the mountains there is a classic display of glacial features: horns, arêtes, U-shaped valleys, cirques, hanging valleys, tarns, and various deposits near the foot of the mountains. The latter take the form of outwash deposits and moraines. The "Potholes," south of Jackson Lake, is an area of outwash with many kettle holes. There is also a fine display of outwash terraces along the Snake River in Jackson Hole. The lakes at the foot of the range—Jenny, Leigh, Phelps, and Jackson—lie in basins formed by morainal dams.

Very active mass-wasting, the result of the glacially over-steepened slopes, on the sides of the cirques and U-shaped valleys can be noted. Rock falls, extensive talus slopes, and landslides are common. Avalanches of snow and active frost-wedging of the bedrock are also notable.

The crest of the range lies on the eastern side, the slope westward from the crest being much less steep in general than that to the east, the side of the fault scarp. The Teton Basin on the west side of the range is another intermontane basin similar to those elsewhere in the province.

Erosion along the crest of the range has exposed a core of Precambrian rocks, granite gneiss, schist, and pegmatite dikes, the latter very obvious on the flanks of many of the peaks. Sedimentary rocks are found on the less deeply eroded western slopes of the range.

A number of other smaller fault-block ranges are found in western Wyoming south of the Grand Tetons, such as Salt, Wyoming, and Hoback mountains.

The western margin of the Wasatch Mountains is straight and follows a fault. The ascent is abrupt from the relatively flat country on which Salt Lake City and Ogden are built. Faceted spurs are notable. The east side of the range is deeply

THE GRAND TETONS, WYOMING. View shows the steep east face, the fault scarp. (Photograph © 1968 by Charles E. Rotkin. From *The U.S.A.: An Aerial Close-up* [Crown])

eroded and quite irregular. The glaciated crest rises over 10,000 feet.

Volcanic rocks appear extensively distributed in the Yellowstone Park and in the Absaroka Mountains immediately to the east of the park.

The Yellowstone Plateau is a forested region lying between 7,500 and 8,500 feet in elevation. The area is surrounded by generally higher mountainous country. Large and relatively flat sections alternate with scarps developed on resistant flows. River valleys, many of which are deep, traverse the region. The canyon of the Yellowstone River is about 1,000 feet deep and is cut into colorful rhyolite flows, all more or less with the same resistance to erosion, which results in the canyon walls' having uniform slopes from the rim down to the water's edge.

A variety of lava types is found in the park. Obsidian Cliff is a landmark. Many of the flows show columnar jointing, such as that at Tower Junction. The recency of the volcanic activity is emphasized by the presence of many hot springs, geysers, and fumaroles. Hot-spring deposits develop terraces and low mounds around the geysers. Calcareous deposits of travertine have built up the layers at Mammoth Hot Springs, and around many of the geysers, siliceous sinter deposits or geyserite are found.

Tongues of ice from the surrounding mountains coalesced to form piedmont glaciers, which in turn left moraines, lakes, swamps, and various meltwater deposits. Terraces of sediments around the sides of Yellowstone Lake mark former levels of the lake, which, because of ice dams, had various levels at different times.

The Absaroka Mountains are cut from a volcanic plateau which has been sculptured into a region of mountainous high relief. The area is 2,000 to 4,000 feet higher than the neighboring Yellowstone Plateau and is composed of older volcanic rocks. The region, also glaciated, was the feeding ground for the tongues of ice, some of which entered Jackson Hole.

NORTHERN ROCKIES

The Northern Rockies include three groups of ranges which differ one from another in structure and general topography. There is a group of mountains developed on an extensive granite batholith, another group with fault-block structure, and a third group of linear ranges where extensive thrust faulting has occurred.

The granite mountains of central Idaho are carved into the Idaho Batholith, which covers roughly 16,000 square miles. Drainage patterns are largely dendritic; the linearity of the majority of the ranges in the Rocky Mountains is notably missing here. The Bitterroot Mountains on the eastern margin of this area are an exception, having a north-south trend, due to a marginal fault on the east.

Most of the valleys in the granite area are narrow and deep. A few small intermontane basins, 10 to 15 miles across, are present. They are filled with Tertiary to Recent sediments.

An accordance of summit levels in the Salmon River and Clearwater groups of mountains is easily noted, and is probably the result of a dissected peneplain. The Coeur d'Alene and Sawtooth mountains, which lie north and south respectively of the other two groups, have much less obviously accordant summits.

At the north and extending into Canada, a marked linearity of the various ranges in a north-south direction is most evident. The valleys have, in general, been eroded along fault-controlled lines of weakness. The two most notable and extensive valleys are the Rocky Mountain and the Purcell Trenches. They show flat floors veneered with alluvium.

The Rocky Mountain Trench lies about 60 miles west of the eastern margin of the Rockies in Montana and extends for some hundreds of miles into Canada. It includes the Bitterroot and Flathead valleys. At various times, ice dammed up parts of the valley to form glacial lakes, such as the one in the Missoula area which was created by the damming of the Clark Fork of the Columbia River. Traces of former shorelines of this lake, marking various stands of the water, can be noted faintly etching the mountain slopes surrounding Missoula.

The Purcell Trench extends northward from Lake Coeur d'Alene into Canada, where it intersects the Rocky Mountain Trench.

At Glacier National Park, there are some small present-day glaciers as well as an excellent display of the work of valley glaciers of the past. The mountains are, in general, not as high as those farther south; the snow line was, and is, much lower, however, and therefore glacial features are more noticeable.

The mountains in the park area are composed of sedimentary rocks, usually in horizontal layers, and differences in resistance to erosion give the cirque walls and mountain slopes a quite-different look from that associated with the erosion of granite elsewhere in the Rockies.

In southwest Montana, there are a number of linear ranges and intervening valley basins oriented in a variety of directions. This is a region of fault blocks. Erosion followed the faulting, and the basins were buried deeply by debris washed from the uplifted blocks. Erosion has been so extensive that the original mountain shapes have been greatly modified. Many of the basins were filled during the early Tertiary by lake, flood-plain, and alluvial fan deposits, as well as by some volcanic ash deposits. In more recent times, erosion has predominated, and much of the debris deposited earlier has been washed away.

HISTORY OF THE ROCKY MOUNTAIN SYSTEM

A much-abbreviated outline of the geologic history of the Rocky Mountain area starts with the folding and faulting of previous rock layers at the end of the Mesozoic era to create a major mountain range. Erosion followed this uplift, creating the peneplains in the mountains. The material washed from the heights was spread out over the adjoining Great Plains area— as well as into the lower-lying areas between the ranges, such as the parks of the Southern Rockies and the Wyoming Basin —as a large wedge of alluvial deposits.

A late-Tertiary arching of the whole area initiated another time of erosion and resulted in partial removal of the sediments from the Great Plains wedge, the Parks, and the Wyoming Basin. The uplift also explains the present elevation of the peneplains in the mountains. The oldest peneplain is the Summit or Flattop, named after the mountain of that name in Colorado; a younger surface at a lower elevation is the Subsummit, or Rocky Mountain or Sherman peneplain.

Extensive glaciation, when the present-day small glacier remnants were greatly extended, impressed steepened slopes and many glacial features on the land. At the present time, there are still some glaciers and much evidence of landslides, rockfalls, and rapid motion of soil debris downslope.

15 | Colorado Plateau

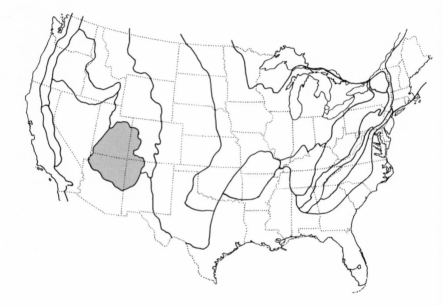

The Colorado Plateau covers approximately 150,000 square miles and lies generally over 1 mile above sea level, except for very limited, deeply eroded areas at the bottoms of canyons. The higher parts may extend to over 11,000 feet in elevation. On the north and east of the Colorado Plateau, the Rocky Mountains rise still higher, and on the west, the Basin and Range province is generally somewhat lower in elevation.

This is an area where essentially horizontal rock layers dominate. A number of plateau levels occur and are separated one from another by faults or by a narrow zone of tilted rocks, a monocline. In addition to producing scarps, the faults have formed lines of weakness which have controlled the location of river valleys. In places, domal upwarps of various sizes and origins have been eroded to create rimming hogback ridges where the dips are steep and cuestas where they are more gentle. However, from an overall standpoint, these features merely modify the basic horizontal structure of the rock layers.

The region is arid to semiarid except at higher elevations, where additional rainfall has led to the production of an extensive forest cover.

Characteristic topography consists of broad, flat surfaces bounded by receding cuesta scarps and cut by deep canyons. This is a region of extensive areas of bedrock with limited vegetation and soil cover, so that the colorful layers are clearly visible in all their brilliance. The colors are due both to the actual colors of the rock layers and to surface stains of weathering.

Much of the topography on canyon wall or retreating scarp face is steplike, reflecting differences in resistance of the various layers of rock. The resistant layers of sandstone and limestone form the steeper parts of the cliffs, and shales form the slopes. In places, the resistant layers may be slightly undercut to give shallow caves similar to those at Mesa Verde in which Indian cliff dwellings have been built.

In about 10 per cent of the plateau area, volcanic cones, lava flows, and volcanic necks and dikes embellish the surface. Such areas of igneous activity are scattered rather widely over the region as a whole.

GRAND CANYON AREA

The Grand Canyon of the Colorado River in Arizona is probably the best known and most dominant feature of the whole area. The river has cut a mile-deep valley into Paleozoic sediments to uncover a Precambrian basement of granite and schist. At the rim of the canyon, rocks of Permian age are

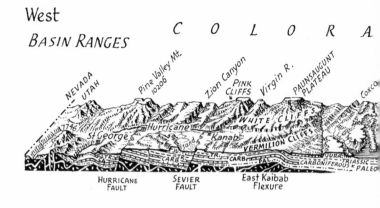

West

BASIN RANGES

C O L O R A

NEVADA UTAH

Pine Valley Mt. 10206

Zion Canyon PINK CLIFFS

Virgin R.

PAUNSAUGUNT PLATEAU

Coxco

1746 St George Hurricane Kanab

WHITE CLIFFS

VERMILION CLIFFS

JURA

TRIASSIC

CARBONIFEROUS PALEO

HURRICANE FAULT

SEVIER FAULT

East Kaibab Flexure

COLORADO PLATEAU, SOUTHERN UTAH, WEST—EAST.

exposed and are seen to overlie rocks of earlier Paleozoic periods, which are visible on the walls of the canyon. At the bottom, near the river level, two older groups of rocks can be noted, both Precambrian in age. The younger group consists of a tilted sequence of sedimentary rocks. They underlie, with an angular unconformity, the Cambrian layers and overlie, in turn, the older Precambrian group, which consists of schist intruded by granite. Such deep erosion into the Precambrian has occurred because of the great uplift of the plateau here.

At the national park area, the canyon is about 12 miles wide

COLORADO PLATEAU, WILLIAMS—GRAND CANYON—BRYCE CANYON.

South

LAVA PLATEAU

C O C O N I N O   P L A T E A U

K A I E

GRAND CANY

Bill Williams 9766 Williams

Red Butte El Tovar

Lodge

CARBONIFEROUS REDWALL

REDW

OLDER PALEOZOIC

ARCHEOZOIC

Unconformit

Bright Ang fault

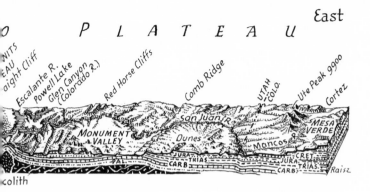

from rim to rim. The dramatic aspect of the scene is due in large part to aridity and the resulting scarcity of vegetation; the rock layers are easily visible in all their colorful variety. Arid-type erosion has also led to the accentuation of an angular type of landform where cliffs of sandstone or limestone meet slopes of shale. The cliffs themselves have angular buttresses and re-entrants. This secondary control by a series of vertical joints as well as faults has given a certain rectangularity to river patterns, which otherwise are roughly dendritic.

The land is very flat for many miles both north and south

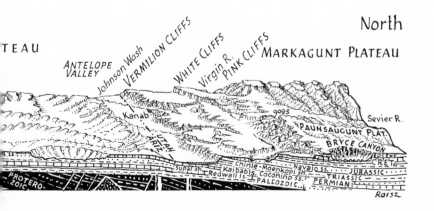

of the rim of the Grand Canyon. About 50 miles south of the canyon, there is a notable area of lava flows and cones where black chunks of scoria can be seen scattered widely. San Francisco Mountain is the most prominent cone here; Sunset Crater was one of the last cinder cones to be formed. The date of its formation was about A.D. 1190.

Meteor Crater lies in this section and is probably extra-terrestrial in origin, the result of a meteorite impact. The floor of this feature lies about 600 feet below the highest parts of the rim.

HIGH PLATEAUS

The High Plateaus, which lie north of the Grand Canyon along the western margin of the province, are a group of plateau surfaces. They occur at varying levels and are bounded by north-south faults which grade in places into monoclines. The general level of the land lies between 9,000 and 11,000 feet above sea level. The Hurricane Fault forms a notable scarp, the Hurricane Ledge, 100 to 1,000 feet high.

A few of the plateau surfaces are capped with lava instead of a resistant sedimentary layer; the majestic Aquarius Plateau is an example.

At the south, the junction with the Grand Canyon section is marked by a number of east-west cuesta scarps which face south. The cuestas are developed on northward dipping layers. Three major scarps must be climbed before reaching the High Plateaus on a trip northward from the Grand Canyon. From south to north, these scarps are the Vermilion, White and Pink cliffs. The first two are Mesozoic in age, and the last is Tertiary. Each marks the location of a resistant layer which at one time extended farther south but has been peeled off the land there by the northward retreat of the cliff face. This recession has been markedly irregular, so that there are deep reentrants and

THE GRAND CANYON, ARIZONA. (Aero Service Division—Litton Industries)

BRYCE CANYON, UTAH. (National Park Service)

promontories as well as outliers of the cliff material left behind. Zion Canyon has been cut into the White Cliffs. Cedar Breaks and Bryce Canyon are cut into the Pink Cliffs, and their irregular front is well known. The dramatic coloring of the rocks at Bryce Canyon is due to iron oxide stains; the red and red brown, to hematite; and the yellows, to limonite. Lime-rich layers form the caps and ledges of the pillars, and the layers of shale and sand which are less limy have been removed to a greater extent to form the grooves, recesses, and small caves.

UINTA BASIN

The Uinta Basin at the northern boundary of the province lies just to the south of the Uinta Mountains. Both structurally and topographically it is the lowest part of the Colorado Plateau province. An east-west synclinal structure has been eroded here. The dips at the north are steeper than those at the south side of the structure. Thus hogbacks have been etched out at the north and cuestas at the south. The Book and the Roan cliffs are cuesta scarps at the south and show the typically irregular retreat of such features. In the central parts of the syncline, stream erosion has greatly cut up the area and has left, in places, interstream, mesalike uplands and, in some places, a badlands topography.

CANYON LANDS

The Canyon Lands in the southeastern parts of Utah is an area of many relatively deep canyons cut into horizontal rock layers. The Marble, Glen, Cataract, and Labyrinth canyons lie here, as well as the deep cut of the San Juan River in southern Utah, where the river has entrenched a meandering course into the land to give the remarkable "goosenecks of the San Juan."

The various parts of this section vary in the amounts of dissection. The Great Sage Plain in the mideastern part of the section is an extensive, sage-covered flat with very few, widely spaced canyons.

The general horizontal structure of the rock layers has, in places, been modified by various domal upwarps, some with igneous and some with salt cores. The erosion of such structures gives an extensive development of hogbacks and cuestas on the flanks. Hogbacks here are often called reefs, such as Capital Reef in Utah.

The San Rafael Swell, 100 by 50 miles, is an asymmetrical anticlinal structure trending northeast-southwest and lying in the northwest part of the section. Elsewhere, many anticlinal valleys can be found, such as Salt, Paradox, and Gypsum valleys. Where broad synclinal structures exist, these may erode into mesalike country.

The Henry Mountains are domal uplifts due to the intrusion of small igneous rock bodies. In some cases, as at Mounts Hillers, Ellen, and Ellsworth, the erosion has been so extensive that the igneous intrusions have been largely uncovered. In other cases erosion has been less, and in the case of Navajo Mountain the presumed intrusion at the center is still hidden. Laccoliths, dikes, and sills can all be noted in the eroded central parts of the domes. Hogbacks occur on the flanks, and the streams which leave the central areas of these domes develop a radial pattern.

NAVAJO SECTION

The Navajo section is an area east of the Grand Canyon and south of the Canyon Lands. It is similar to the Canyon Lands, but the amount of dissection is somewhat less. The only major perennial stream to cross this area is the San Juan. Canyons are somewhat wider and less deep here. Deformation has been somewhat less here also; thus hogbacks are less common and the landforms tend to be mesas, buttes, cuestas, and rock terraces.

Many volcanic necks and flows are present. The classic volcanic neck, Shiprock, lies in northwestern New Mexico. Towering 1,400 feet above the flat land, it has quite noticeable radiating resistant dikes which form stony walls starting at the central peak. Agathla, in northeastern Arizona, is another excellent example of a volcanic neck. It extends about 1,200 feet above its surroundings.

The Painted Desert is an area of very low rainfall and fantastically colorful clays. Water-worn slopes and gullies, even here, give evidence of the very effective ability of running water to erode. Petrified tree trunks weather out of many of the layers and lie scattered about on the surface, looking just as if someone had been chopping wood.

SOUTHEASTERN VOLCANIC AREA

At the extreme southeastern part of the Colorado Plateau province, there are many lava flows, lava-capped mesas, and, especially in the Mount Taylor area, volcanic peaks.

The Zuni Uplift, southeast of Gallup, is a major anticlinal structure here, in which erosion has uncovered, at the center, rocks of Precambrian age and has produced a series of rimming hogbacks and alternating valleys on the flanks.

16 | Columbia Plateau

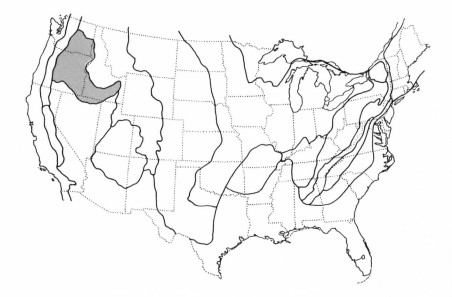

The Columbia Plateau, a region of over 100,000 square miles, is one of the world's major areas of lava. It is bordered on the west by the Cascades, a majestic range of strato-volcanoes, and on the north and east by the higher-standing Rockies. On the south there is a gradational boundary with the Basin and Range province.

The plateau is, in general, arid to semiarid, lying as it does in the "rain shadow" cast by the Cascades. The southwestern parts have interior drainage, and salt lakes abound.

Lavas vary in age from early Tertiary to Recent. The most recent flows, less than 1,000 years old, appear on the Snake River plain in southern Idaho. Elsewhere, earlier flows have been faulted, warped up or down, and eroded to form regions of moderate relief. Also a few mountain areas of older rock protrude as islands through the sea of lava.

Ash layers and sedimentary deposits are found interbedded between the lava flows, as well as soils developed at times of quiescence between times of volcanic activity. Many of the interflow deposits were laid down in temporary lakes formed where a flow dammed up a river valley.

Individual lava flows vary from 20 to 200 feet in thickness and in places have built up sequences over 2 miles thick. Most commonly the lavas are basalt, although there are areas where lighter-colored andesites and rhyolites can be found.

Columnar jointing is very obvious wherever earlier flows have been cut into and a side view can be obtained, as on canyon walls and cliff faces. The topmost parts of many flows may show a somewhat porous texture, where gas bubbles accumulated as the lava was cooling. The middle parts, of the thicker flows especially, are apt to be slightly coarser grained than either the top or the bottom because of slower cooling.

Most of the lava in the plateau area welled up along extensive fractures in a generally quiet, not explosive, fashion. The feeding cracks of earlier flows can be seen wherever erosion has uncovered these fractures now filled with cooled lava. They appear as dikes cutting across earlier flows.

A region of highlands in the central parts of the province divides it into three parts: the Columbia Basin at the north, the Highlands in the middle, and the region of Lava Plains on the south.

In the Columbia Basin section, rolling to moderately hilly land has developed in what is structurally a broad basin. Most of the surface is covered by flows of Miocene age. Rocks of older age may be found protruding in places through the sea of lava. Such features are called steptoes, after Steptoe Butte, a hill of quartzite entirely surrounded by later lava.

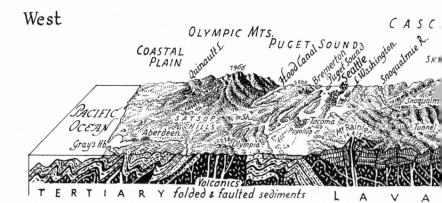

West

OLYMPIC MTS.

COASTAL PLAIN

CASC

PUGET SOUND

PACIFIC OCEAN

TERTIARY folded & faulted sediments   LAVA

COLUMBIA PLATEAU, OLYMPIC MOUNTAINS—LAKE COEUR D'ALENE.

In the east, a thick, weathered soil composed of loess forms the rich Palouse soils. Here, somewhat farther away from the rain shadow cast by the Cascades, the rainfall is slightly greater than the average on the plateau.

In the center of the Columbia Basin section, there is a remarkable section, the Channeled Scablands, quite obviously eroded by vast quantities of rapidly flowing water. Dry channels (coulees) form an intricately interlocking, braided system of stream-cut valleys. "Dry" waterfalls, with plunge pools at their bases and water-rounded sand and gravel deposits many feet above the coulee floors, attest to the former presence of floods of water streaming southward across this now-barren region. A fantastic network of intercoulee benches, mesas, and buttes is left. It has been suggested that glacial meltwaters took this course at a time when the present course of the Columbia River was choked by ice.

The Grand Coulee is 50 miles long, 1,000 feet deep, and one half to 4 miles wide. In places the granite floor on which the lavas were extruded has been exposed. Moses Coulee lies to the

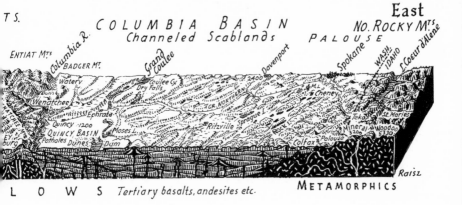

west of Grand Coulee; it was probably a former path of the Columbia River.

The Highland section in northeastern Oregon is an area of deeply dissected, faulted, and tilted basalt flows. At various times, basins were formed and filled with sediments, including much fine volcanic ash. The John Day Basin is a classic example. The beds here are unusually rich in plant and vertebrate fossils. In the higher mountains, prebasalt metamorphic and igneous rocks are exposed.

The Lava Plains section lies in the southern part of the province. It is an area where flows are younger and less deformed than those in the Columbia Basin section, and lake and stream deposits are more commonly interbedded with the various flows.

On the east, in southern Idaho, the Snake River plain presents a remarkably flat surface; it looks as if a great sheet of lava had recently flooded out over the land. A very thin soil has developed in places; in other places, the flows are so recent that there is no soil. At the Craters of the Moon National Monu-

"DRY FALLS," GRAND COULEE, WASHINGTON. Layers of lava flows, one on top of the other, can be noted on the cliff faces. (U.S. Dept. of the Interior, Bureau of Reclamation)

ment there are cinder cones, spatter cones, aa and pahoehoe flows, lava caves and tunnels, and tree molds. Some of the flows here are no more than a few hundreds of years old.

The Snake River plain, which slopes westward very gently, is cut by the Snake River, which has virtually no surface tributaries in this area from the north. However, water flows under the surface, through very porous and permeable layers of lava and sedimentary rock, to emerge on the walls of the Snake River valley as enormous springs. A well-known group of springs is that of the Thousand Springs between Twin Falls and Bliss, Idaho.

In Oregon, just east of the Cascades, the lava plains region is very dry. The Great Sandy Desert, southeast of Bend, Oregon, is a pumice-covered dry waste, where a few isolated low cones break the generally monotonous surface. The Deschutes River, which drains this area, has a remarkably large and uniform flow for a desert stream. This is explained by the fact that its waters come from the Cascades and cover most of the distance from the mountains via underground passages to appear as springs from permeable layers in the lavas.

On the south, the boundary of the Lava Plains with the Basin and Range province is transitional in nature. Features characteristic of one province appear in the neighboring one to a minor degree.

17 | Basin and Range

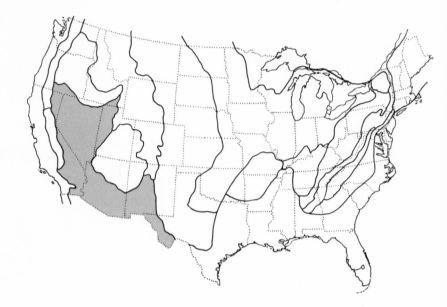

The Basin and Range province is an area of distant vistas where landforms many miles away are clear in the dry desert air. Isolated mountain ranges, which trend roughly north to south, rise abruptly 3,000 to 5,000 feet above intermontane desert basins. From almost any vantage point, there is striking evidence for both destruction of the land and for deposition. The mountains have a tattered appearance, with ragged, worn-down peaks and flanks where gullies and water-worn slopes are plentiful. In some places alluvial fans are found at the base of the steeper slopes and may form a more-or-less continuous apron (bajada) of debris along a mountain front. Elsewhere, there may be, instead of alluvial fans, a gently sloping, eroded rock surface, thinly veneered with sediments. Usually the desert basins have a thicker alluvial deposit nearer the center, where a temporary lake (playa) may be present after a time of rain. The finest sediment is found at the center, becoming somewhat coarser as the mountain front is approached. In some areas dried-out lake floors may extend to the mountain flank itself, without any intervening gentle slope.

The low rainfall, which for most of the province is less than 10 inches per year, is adequate to support only an arid to semi-arid type of vegetation, and most of the region has interior drainage; that is, streams do not reach the sea but evaporate, sink into the ground, or enter a temporary lake at the center of the desert basin. Such playa lakes, which have no surface outlets, dry out at times of drought, and at times of increased rains may become much larger. Their depth and surface area are thus constantly changing in response to the supply of water. Such ephemeral lakes are usually salt; when they dry out, a coating of some variety of white salt is left on the surface.

Stream valleys in a desert are usually dry; it is only after a rain that water can be found in them. However, the rare torrential rains, so characteristic of such areas, are extremely effective agents of erosion. It is quite apparent to anyone who has seen the effects of water erosion that rain, rare though it be, is generally much more effective in moving material than the wind, even in a desert.

It is obvious that in this province, the mountains are in the process of being carried bit by bit into the intervening low areas. Some mountains have obviously been attacked by this process for a longer period of time than others, and there may now be only a remnant of a mountain mass sticking up through a thick filling of sediments.

In some locations, sand dunes may dominate the scenery; they mark areas where the wind is apparently more important as a transportation agent than running water. Dunes are usually composed of quartz sand, but, as at the White Sands National Monument, they may be composed of glistening gypsum

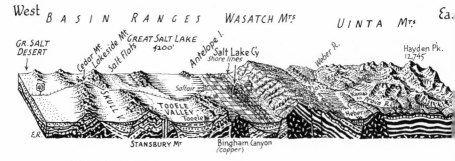

BASIN AND RANGE, GREAT SALT LAKE—WASATCH MOUNTAINS.

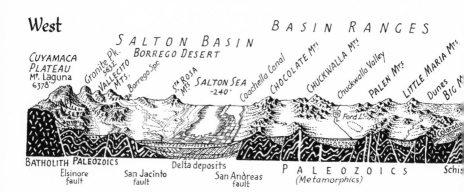

BASIN AND RANGE, SALTON SEA.

sand, the type of weathered bedrock in the vicinity determining the composition of the dunes.

The abrasive action of blowing sand produces ventifacts, or wind-faceted pebbles, which are often found on alluvial fans in association with desert pavement, or lag gravel. Such a surface is created when the wind blows away the finer dust and sand of a fan, leaving the coarser gravel. In places the surface of desert pavement is so level and the pebbles interlock so well that it looks almost man-made.

There are over 150 separate ranges in this province. Many of the fault blocks forming them are asymmetric in cross-section, the steeper side marking the side along which the faulting took place. In some cases both sides of a block have been faulted. The internal structure of the fault blocks is often very complex, indicating a history of earlier faulting, folding, and igneous activity. Some ranges are capped with a layer of lava. The recency of the faulting in many cases is demonstrated by the presence of small fault scarps which cut the alluvial fan material at the base of a number of the ranges. They indicate renewed faulting following the major uplift of the range. For instance, in 1872, a major earthquake shook Owens Valley in California; a zone of visible faults associated with it now extends for 100 miles along the valley.

Permanent lakes are much fewer in number than playa lakes, examples being Great Salt Lake in Utah, Pyramid Lake and Lake Winnemucca in Nevada, and Mono Lake in California. In many places, there is evidence of the former presence of lakes which now do not exist and of the much greater extent of present lakes. The evidence consists of flat lake floors and wave and current-fashioned features incised on mountain slopes well above the present level of the basin floors.

Great Salt Lake varies in depth and area from season to season. It is the remnant of a much larger lake, Lake Bonneville, which existed at the time when glaciers were extensive over North America. Lake Bonneville at one time also included Utah Lake and Sevier Lake.

Death Valley, one of the most dramatic areas in the province, shows to perfection both erosional and depositional features. Many alluvial fans are found, such as the large Hanaupah Fan, which has an extensive system of braided channels on its surface. Ventifacts, desert pavement, and desert varnish are well developed. Salt flats abound. In places the surface of the salt is very rough and corrugated, as at the Devil's Golf Course.

This is due to alternate solution by rare rains followed by deposition as the water evaporated.

The strand lines of a glacial-age lake 400 to 500 feet above the floor of the present valley mark the former presence of the now-vanished Lake Manly.

Badlands topography is found where layers are soft and easily eroded, and areas of sand dunes where there is a supply of sand. The recency of faulting here is indicated by the well-

DEATH VALLEY, CALIFORNIA. (Spence Air Photos)

developed system of scarplets along the east side of the valley cutting the alluvial fans. They range in height to a few feet in places.

Recent volcanic activity is obvious in the north end of the Death Valley area at Ubehebe Craters.

Farther south in California, the Salton Sea in the Imperial Valley lies in a lowland cut off from the Gulf of Lower California by the growth of the Colorado River delta. Many sand dunes, some of them barchans, are found; a former shoreline, which is 40 to 50 feet high high, faintly notches the slopes of the surrounding mountains.

18 | Sierra Nevada

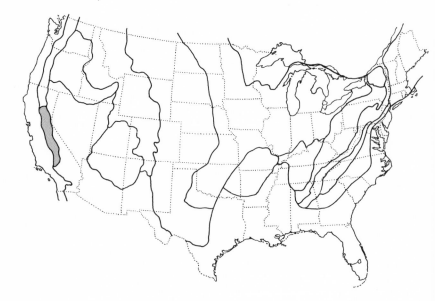

The Sierra Nevada are carved from the largest continuous mountain block in the United States. They extend for over 400 miles north to south and are 40 to 60 miles wide. The Central Valley of California lies on the west, and the Basin and Range province on the east. (See Raisz Structure, Section 16.) The block was uplifted along a marginal fault on the east side. This has resulted in an asymmetrical mountain range with the crest line near the eastern margin. The slopes here are precipitous; steep U-shaped valleys are obvious; and moraines marking the dump from the glaciers flowing down this side are found at the base of the slopes. A number of both terminal and lateral moraines are especially well developed in the Mono Lake area. Here also the Mono Craters are major landmarks. They are composed of pumice and obsidian.

One of the major scenic attractions of the area is Lake Tahoe, which lies at an elevation of 6,200 feet and is surrounded by 9,000 to 10,000-foot peaks. The lake, roughly 12 by 22 miles, is bounded by subsidiary faults which are approximately parallel to the major boundary fault.

About sixty small glaciers still exist on the higher slopes of the range. They indicate what was a major agent of erosion in the recent past, when many streams of ice flowed down from the peaks along preglacial stream-cut valleys. Thus the region now has many rock basin lakes, cirques, arêtes, horns, and grooved and polished bedrock surfaces, as well as U-shaped valleys. This gives the higher slopes of the Sierra Nevada a characteristic jagged topography, where slopes are steep and where rockfalls and landslides are common.

Yosemite Valley, on the western slope of the range, is a classic glacially shaped feature which was the dumping ground of stream deposits after the ice left, so that now the valley has a flat floor over which the Merced River meanders. Beautiful hanging valleys and waterfalls, such as Bridalveil and Yosemite, are present. Exfoliation domes are well developed in the massive granite peaks which surround the valley, and spheroidal weathering has produced residual boulders which can be seen from some of the roads in the area.

In the higher parts of the mountains, there are small, relatively flat areas which may mark remnants of an uplifted peneplain. The gently sloping upper reaches of a number of the peaks, such as Mounts Whitney, Bernard, Langley, and Cirque Peak are examples.

The geologic history of the Sierra Nevada includes the intrusion of a large granite batholith into a series of sedimentary

SIERRA NEVADA. View is from the east, showing the fault scarp. (W. C. Mendenhall, U.S. Geological Survey)

rocks at the end of the Jurassic period, followed by the extensive erosion of the rocks and the development of the now-uplifted peneplain. Block faulting, beginning in the Tertiary and continuing through the Pleistocene, led to the formation of the major uplifted mass of the mountains. Continuous weathering and river erosion, especially with glacial erosion during the last 1,000,000 or so years, has produced the present scene.

19 | Cascades

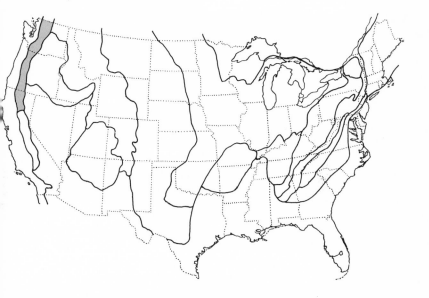

A series of majestic strato-volcanoes extends from northern California through Oregon and Washington. They lie on top of, and put the finishing touches to, an uplifted section of the country. In the southern parts there is more volcanic activity than toward the north, where there has been a great deal of erosion of uplifted plateaulike blocks, on which a few widely spaced volcanic cones have been erupted. A number of the peaks in the north are carved of granite and metamorphic rocks.

The volcanoes, which rise thousands of feet above their surroundings, are landmarks for many miles. The major cones from south to north are Lassen and Shasta in California; Crater Lake, Three Sisters, Jefferson, and Hood in Oregon; Saint

THE THREE SISTERS, OREGON. Typical strato-volcanoes. (Oregon State Highway Commission)

Helens, Adams, Rainier, Glacier, and Hood in Washington. (See Raisz Structure, Section 13.)

Mount Lassen is the only volcano in the group which has been active in the present century. Mount Shasta has a noticeable parasitic cone, Shastina, on its side. Many of the cones have present-day glaciers on their upper slopes, and there is clear evidence, in the form of U-shaped valleys, that they at one time extended much farther downslope than they do now.

One of the best-known cones is that associated with Crater Lake in Oregon. The top of the former volcano, Mount Mazama, is missing; its destruction has left the very large and dramatic caldera now filled by Crater Lake. The lake, about 6,000 feet above sea level, is 2,000 feet deep, and the rim of the caldera rises 500 to 2,000 feet above lake level. Wizard Island is a small cinder cone which protrudes above lake level.

Before the caldera was formed, primarily by the engulfment of part of the former top of the volcano, a number of glaciers flowed down the sides of the cone and left U-shaped valleys. Two of these valleys can now be noted as starting at Sun and Kerr notches on the rim and extending downward from there. Flows and interbedded glacial deposits can be noted on the sides of the caldera. Inasmuch as the walls of the Crater Lake basin have been essentially blasted out of the material of the cone, it is understandable that there should be exposed to view dikes of lava which intruded into the cone material after it was constructed. The Devil's Backbone and Phantom Ship are composed of dike material which is slightly more resistant than the rocks into which they were intruded.

Pumice is much in evidence in various places in the area. It lies in many of the valleys descending from the top of the mountain, deposited at times when glowing avalanches of pumice fragments emerged explosively from the cone. In Sand Creek Canyon, at the Pinnacles, a field of pumice has a special appearance. Former gas vents extended up through the pumice, and where the gas came into contact with the pumice, it altered it into a somewhat harder and more resistant material. The separate pinnacles of pumice mark former escape tubes through which gas emerged. Many are hollow.

20 | Pacific Border

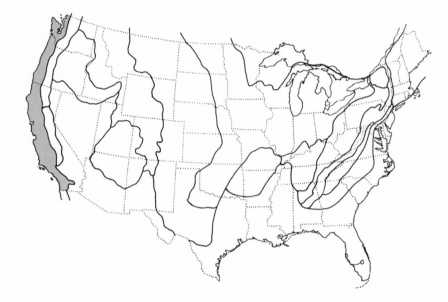

The Pacific Border province consists of a series of mountain ranges along the Pacific Coast. These are bordered on the east by an almost-continuous lowland belt, with two major interruptions: the Klamath Mountains in southern Oregon and the Transverse Ranges in southern California.

The lowland belt starts with Puget Sound in Washington and extends southward to the Willamette Valley in Oregon. (See Raisz Structure, Section 13.) This lowland is roughly 400 miles long, north to south, and 50 miles wide. The north end has been drowned to form Puget Sound, where there are many inlets and islets. Farther south, the Chehalis and Cowlitz rivers drain the lowland in Washington, and the Willamette River the Oregon section.

After the break of the Klamath Mountains, the lowland continues southward through the Sacramento and San Joaquin valleys of California to the Transverse Ranges. South of these lies the Los Angeles lowland.

The Great Valley of California lies between the Sierra Nevada and the California Coast Ranges. The Klamath Mountains cut off the valley at the north, and the Tehachapi Mountains at the south. The northern part is drained by the Sacramento River, and the southern by the San Joaquin River. These two rivers join to drain out to sea via San Francisco Bay. The major part of the valley is underlain by the down-dropped part of the Sierra Nevada fault block. At the center of the valley, there are 25,000 to 30,000 feet of sediments lying on the bedrock.

The Sacramento River section of the Great Valley is an extensive, flat, alluvium-filled area. Natural levees along the winding river and various flood-plain deposits are common. The present valley floor has been cut into a former higher level. This has left a number of flat-topped sand and gravel terraces bordering the present valley. The general flat country is interrupted by the Marysville Buttes, which are volcanic hills rising 2,000 feet above the general level of the land.

The San Joaquin section is more arid than that at the north, the southern third having interior drainage. Two major playa lake basins are found here: the Tulare at the north and the Buena Vista at the south. They are separated by the alluvial fan of the Kern River. Other alluvial fans and small playa lakes are common. The major relief feature in this section is the Kettleman Hills, which cover an area approximately 5 by 30 miles. Streams have greatly dissected the hills, breaching the three major anticlines of the area, and now there is a close adjustment of topography to the structure.

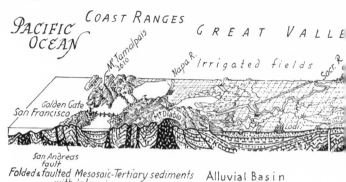

West

PACIFIC OCEAN — COAST RANGES — GREAT VALLE

Mt. Tamalpais 2610

Napa R. — Irrigated fields — Sacr. R.

Golden Gate
San Francisco — Mt. Diablo — Lodi

San Andreas fault

Folded & faulted Mesosoic-Tertiary sediments with intrusions   Alluvial Basin

PACIFIC BORDER, SAN FRANCISCO—LAKE TAHOE.

The mountains along the coast, from north to south, are the Olympics in Washington; the Oregon Coast Ranges and Klamaths in southern Oregon; and the California Coast Ranges, Transverse Ranges, and Peninsular Ranges in southern California.

There is heavy precipitation in the Olympic Mountains. They show typical glacier-carved features, such as cirques, U-shaped valleys, horns, and arêtes. Mount Olympus (7,954 feet) is the highest point. A small number of short glaciers are still present at the higher elevations.

The Oregon Coast Ranges extend from approximately the Chehalis River southward to the Klamaths in southern Oregon. The peaks are generally less than 4,000 feet in elevation. There is a noticeable north-south alignment of valleys, the result of erosion along the weaker layers in a region of folded rocks.

The Klamath Mountains show many peaks over 6,000 feet in elevation with obvious evidence of glaciation. It is a region of largely unoriented, rather sprawling mountain masses. The region resembles the Sierra Nevada in geology more than the other

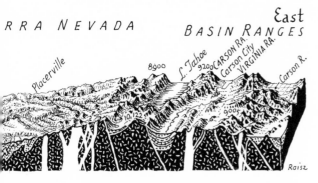

Placerville   8900   L. Tahoe 9200 CARSON RA. Carson City VIRGINIA RA. CARSON RA. Carson R.

Raisz

Granite and Volcanics   Complex fault blocks

coast ranges, a resemblance reinforced by the presence of gold-bearing gravels along many of the rivers.

In California a series of linear ranges, which trend northwest-southeast, extends for 400 miles along the coast from the Klamath Mountains to the Tranverse Ranges. The elevation varies generally between 2,000 and 4,000 feet, with some peaks up to 6,000 feet in elevation. The location of the valleys and ridges is largely controlled by the faulting and folding of the rocks.

Mountains rise abruptly from the ocean, the seaward edge being marked by active wave erosion and showing uplifted terraces and cliffs. The San Francisco embayment breaks the almost-continuous line of mountains.

The region is arid to semiarid; stream deposition in the forms of fans and valley deposits is very obvious. Slumps and landslides on the steep slopes are common, especially along the coast.

The major, best-known fault is the San Andreas, which cuts across the ranges from the sea at Point Arena north of San Francisco and extends southeastward for 550 miles to disappear under a sedimentary cover in the Imperial Valley. Such a rift produces a zone of weakness in the rocks which is more easily eroded than elsewhere and results in such features as Tomales Bay at the north along the coast, San Andreas Lake south of San Francisco, and many other linear features farther south. The area west of the fault has moved northward with respect to the land to the east.

The Transverse Ranges trend almost east-west. This chain of mountain ranges, which includes the Santa Ynez, Santa Monica, San Gabriel, and San Bernardino ranges has an underwater, seaward extension which protrudes as the islands of Santa Cruz, Santa Rosa, and San Miguel. Dramatic evidence of river erosion, mass-wasting in the mountains, and the deposition of much of the transported debris on the bordering flat areas in the form of fans is obvious. The cores of the mountains are composed of granite; there are metamorphic rocks on the flanks. Faults and folded rocks are much in evidence.

The Peninsular Ranges include mountains of relatively complex structure and various lowland areas, such as the Los Angeles Basin. The elongated ranges and intermontane valleys trend, in general, northwest-southeast. Alignments in the topography are largely the result of fault control in the location of valleys, and the intermontane basins are generally bounded by faults. The rocks are primarily metamorphic and igneous.

Along the whole Pacific coast, there is extensive evidence of wave and current erosion. Sea cliffs, headlands of resistant rock, sea stacks, caves, and arches are all common. Between headlands, there are small coves with short beaches. Raised wave-cut terraces are common, and sea stacks may sometimes be found on such uplifted wave-cut benches. The series of terraces in southern California on the ocean side of Palos Verdes Hills is classic. They mark successive stands of the sea with respect to the land. The highest terrace is over 1,000 feet above the present stand of the sea.

Surge channels are common and found where some weaker

SEA CLIFFS AND TERRACE ON OREGON COAST. (Oregon State Highway Commission)

material, such as a dike or jointed rock, has been eroded at the expense of the material lying on either side.

In addition to the striking evidence of the rise of the land, there is also evidence of flooding. A number of estuaries mark the flooded lower reaches of river valleys. Puget Sound and San Francisco Bay are such areas. However, on any detailed map others can be noted—some already filled by deltaic and flood-plain deposits; others perhaps cut off from the open sea by a sand bar.

In places the narrow strip of coastal land along the sea is covered by sand dunes. Many such coastal dunes are found along the Oregon coast, where they may dam up a tidal inlet to form a lake.

21 | *Alaska*

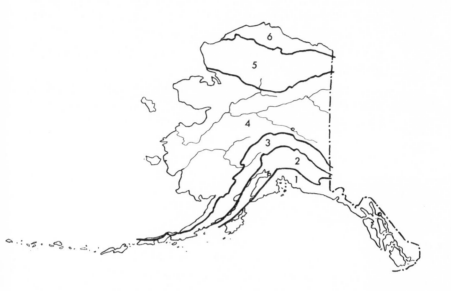

Alaska, in area equal to about one-fifth of the continental United States, can conveniently be divided into four major divisions, each of which is the continuation of a major geologic province from farther south in the United States and Canada. From south to north these divisions are Pacific Mountain system (1, 2, 3), Interior province (4), Brooks Range (5), Arctic Coastal Plain (6).

The Pacific Mountain system is composed of three parts: the Pacific Border Ranges at the south (1), the Alaska Mountains– Aleutian region farther north (3), and in between, a series of disconnected lowlands, the Coastal Trough province (2). The lowlands from west to east are Cook Inlet, Susitna Valley, and

Copper River Lowland. These three parts are the Alaskan equivalent of the Coast Range, Lowland, and Cascade group of provinces in Washington and Oregon.

The Interior province is generally a lowland area of plains, plateaus, and low mountains, comparable to the region between the Rockies and the Sierra Nevada–Cascade province.

The Brooks Range is a continuation of the Rocky Mountains of the United States and Canada, and the Arctic Coastal Plain is the geologic equivalent of the Great Plains in the United States and Canada. Here, however, it is bordered by the Arctic Ocean instead of the Interior Lowland as in the United States or the Precambrian shield as in Canada.

The general trend of the provinces in Alaska, instead of being roughly north to south as in the United States and Canada, is in an east-west direction.

PACIFIC MOUNTAIN SYSTEM

As a whole this region includes very high mountains, superlative glacial scenery, fjords, and active volcanoes.

The Alaska Range is a major mountain mass composed of a series of separate units which extend from the Canadian border westward to join the Alaska Peninsula. On the north it is bounded by the Interior province. Many valley glaciers are present, and the heights show extensive glacial dissection. A granite batholith, forming the core of much of the range, outcrops in magnificent cliffs on the flanks of Mount McKinley, the highest peak in North America, 20,300 feet above sea level.

From Mount Spurr, about 80 miles west of Anchorage, through the Alaska Peninsula and thence to the end of the Aleutian Island chain at Attu Island, 1,000 miles away, a string

CHUGACH RANGE, ALASKA. Note medial moraines and jagged glacial topography. (Photo by Laurence Lowry)

of active or recently active volcanoes surmounts a more-or-less continuous ridge. The cones resemble those in the Cascades, and calderas are found at the summits of a few of them, such as that at Mount Katmai, formed in 1912 at the time of a major eruption.

THE WHITE MOUNTAINS, ALASKA. A view in the Interior province. Note solifluction lobes on the slopes. (Photo by Laurence Lowry)

The Pacific Border Ranges extend northward from the panhandle of Alaska through the Saint Elias Mountains and then westward to include the Chugach and Kenai Mountains and Kodiak Island.

The ranges of southeast Alaska in the panhandle region show a marked northwest-southeast alignment, which is the result of faulting as well as the erosion of weaker bands in an area of metamorphic rock. The location and shape of such an elongated, deep estuary as Chatham Strait is fault controlled.

The Saint Elias Mountains, at the junction of the Alaskan Panhandle and the main part of the state, have been called by many the most spectacular mountains in North America. This is a region of superb glaciers which form an essentially continuous network of ice fields and ice streams. Steep cliffs, horns, and arêtes compose a backdrop for the ice-filled valleys. The sinuous passage of the ice streams as they ooze down the valleys is marked by medial moraines riding on the surface and embedded in the ice. Drainage is essentially all by ice; there are no rivers or lakes.

The Malaspina Glacier north of Yakutat Bay covers about 850 square miles along the coast at the base of the Saint Elias Mountains. The fantastically contorted pattern of the morainal material riding on the surface of the ice shows the complicated motions of this semistagnant mass of ice, the classic example of a piedmont glacier.

Starting at the Saint Elias Mountains, the Chugach and Kenai Mountains, together with their continuation in Kodiak Island, form a mountain mass extending along the coast. Along the shore there are many fjords, islands, and raised wave-cut terraces. The mountains are glaciated and very rugged in parts.

The Wrangell Mountains, lying between the Chugach and Alaska Ranges, also are rugged and extensively glaciated. A number of volcanoes, both composite and shield, are found here.

INTERIOR PROVINCE

The Interior province is an area of relatively low, very much dissected uplands with an intervening network of many meandering rivers which flow over extensive flood plains. The general level of the land decreases from the Canadian border westward, from a maximum elevation of about 6,000 feet to 4,000 feet.

Most of the drainage of the region is by the Yukon and Kuskokwim River systems. The flow of the rivers is sluggish for much of the way. The Yukon River, in places, has a flood plain over 50 miles wide, but narrows wherever it cuts through one of the upland areas. Oxbow lakes and meander scrolls give an intricate and fascinating pattern to many of the flood plain areas.

The rivers freeze over in winter, but when they do flow, in spring and summer, they carry an enormous load of sediments, derived from the glacial deposits of the past as well as from the glacial erosion of the present.

Uplands between the rivers are moderately low in elevation. They are largely tundra-covered, with V-shaped, youthful valleys incising the otherwise rounded contours.

At no time was the Interior province entirely ice-covered. Glaciers extended farther into it both from the Brooks Range at the north and from the Alaska Range from the south, but these ice masses never met.

Debris from former, greatly extended glaciers is especially widespread near the base of the Pacific Mountain System. Moraines, kames, eskers, and glacial lake deposits are numerous; mud and silt were carried farther out from the mountains by meltwaters. At the present time much of the material composing these former deposits is being eroded by streams, many of which show a heavily loaded braided pattern. Low terraces are left along the sides of the valleys, where erosion has partially removed the former valley fill. In such areas placer gold is found

ARCTIC COASTAL PLAIN, ALASKA. Lakes and "patterned ground."
(Photo by Laurence Lowry)

in some of the gravel deposits, and gold dredges have left their characteristic gravel ridges.

Permafrost is found in a discontinuous fashion over much of the region. Such a condition leads to poor drainage and to various features due to frost action. Solifluction lobes and evidence of soil creep are very noticeable on the slopes. Landslides also are common. They characteristically leave a bowl-shaped depression at the upper end and a bulging, hummocky pile of debris at the base.

Dunes are locally prominent where dried-out, sandy flood plains supply the material. Dust from the same source forms loess deposits, which are extensive.

BROOKS RANGE

The Brooks Range, an east-west range, separates the Arctic Coastal Plain from the Interior province. It is roughly 600 miles long and 80 miles wide, with elevations which reach up to between 8,000 and 9,000 feet. It is a treeless region and has not been as noticeably glaciated as the Pacific Mountain system.

The structure and age of the rocks is similar to the Rocky Mountains farther south. A folded sequence of Paleozoic and Mesozoic rocks has been uplifted and eroded. The layers of the sedimentary rocks are very noticeable on the sides of the mountains where a cliff-and-bench topography is often formed.

The mountains are now covered with perennial snow and there are a few glaciers. U-shaped valleys, lakes, cirques, and other glacial features are found, but are not nearly as well developed as are those in the higher Pacific Mountain system.

A belt of foothills on the northern flanks of the range is festooned with moraines; outwash terraces extend northward from the moraines.

ARCTIC COASTAL PLAIN

In winter the Arctic Coastal Plain is a wasteland of frozen lakes, rivers, and snow-covered flats. In summer it turns into a waterlogged world of lakes, marshes, and slowly moving rivers. Surface drainage is exceedingly slow, and water cannot drain downward because the ground is permanently frozen under the shallow surface zone of melting.

Near the foothills of the Brooks Range, the rivers which drain northward have cut relatively narrow flood plain valleys into the plain, which is about 600 feet above sea level here. The bordering river bluffs are 50 to 300 feet high. As the coast is approached, the level of the plain gradually becomes lower, so that the rivers, instead of being confined to shallow valleys, meander through a maze of lakes and lagoons. Offshore, there are a number of sand bars; sand spits may occur in places.

Freeze-and-thaw features associated with permafrost are very common. Ice-wedge polygons up to 300 feet in diameter, pingoes 20 to 200 feet in height, and thaw lakes are found in abundance.

22 | *Hawaiian Islands*

The Hawaiian Islands afford classic examples of many aspects of volcanic activity. A great variety of cones of all sizes is present, from small spatter cones and cinder cones to enormous shield volcanoes, such as the active Mauna Loa, which towers 13,680 feet above sea level.

The major group of islands, Niihau (1), Kauai (2), Oahu (3), Molokai (4), Lanai (5), Kahoolawe (6), Maui (7) and Hawaii (8), lies at the southeastern end of an underwater volcanic ridge which extends approximately 1,600 miles across the central Pacific Ocean. The only active volcanoes at the present time are on the island of Hawaii, the most easterly and the largest in the island group. Five shield volcanies have coalesced to form this island. They are Kohola (A), Mauna Kea (B), Hualalai (C), Mauna Loa (D) and Kilauea (E). Mauna Loa and Kilauea are the only ones now active.

Mauna Loa covers an area 60 by 30 miles, or about 50 per cent of the island. It is composed primarily of basalt, and has slopes which vary from 4 to 10 degrees. Pyroclastic material makes up less than 5 per cent of the mass. The lava is of the aa and pahoehoe types in about equal amounts.

The construction of such a cone includes, in addition to summit eruptions, many eruptions from the flanks, where lava emerges through an extensive network of rifts. Such a system of feeding cracks can be seen on inactive cones where erosion has uncovered numerous dikes composed of the hardened material which now fills former rifts.

Small collapse structures, grabens, with fault scarps are found here and there on the surface of the active cones. Spatter cones, cinder cones, and pit craters are common along the rift zones. The pit craters are collapse features which vary from 100 feet to half a mile in diameter and from 50 to 800 feet in depth. Lava tubes and tunnels occur where lava has crusted over on the surface and the still-liquid material has drained out from beneath.

The caldera on Kilauea measures about 2 by 3 miles and has an area of more-or-less continuously hot liquid near one side. This is the fire pit of Halemaumau.

Deposits of pyroclastic material are locally abundant on the islands. Diamond Head on Oahu, for instance, is a cone composed of tuff; that is, indurated ash, cinders, and dust.

Rainfall on the islands is markedly variable from place to place. In this region of trade winds the windward (northeast) side has very heavy rainfall and the leeward side has much less.

Lava is, in general, very porous; as a result, well-defined stream channels are lacking on the newer lava flows. However, weathering and stream erosion, especially in the rainy areas, are

very effective in forming deep valleys with precipitous walls. The volcanic slopes of all the islands, except the most recently formed lava slopes on the island of Hawaii, have been deeply incised by canyons with high gradients and very steep walls. The close spacing of such ravines has given a washboard effect to many mountain slopes. Also, a smaller-scale grooving of valley walls and cliff faces is very obvious everywhere.

Valleys on the slopes of the cones characteristically become larger by incorporating neighboring channels. Such a process of valley growth is common where a series of closely spaced streams all flow in the same direction.

Some of the major valleys, unlike the average stream-cut valley, are amphitheater-shaped and resemble a cirque in their upper parts. Here the cutting is, however, not due to ice but is probably the result of rapid chemical weathering in a humid tropical climate combined with the very heavy rainfall. Such valleys develop on slopes which are more than 3 degrees and where there are alternating weak cinder and resistant basalt layers which dip in the same direction as the stream flows. The resistant layers cause steep slopes, often with waterfalls, which are undercut and become higher with headward erosion.

Drowned valleys along the coast, as well as uplifted marine terraces, demonstrate a changing sea level, both up and down with respect to the land. In places, uplifted coral limestone gives the usual features of sinkholes, caves, stalactites, and stalagmites.

At the present time, there are narrow but well-developed coastal plains only on Oahu and Niihau Islands. Where wave erosion is rapid, cliffs hundreds and, in places, thousands of feet high have been cut. Sea stacks cluster off eroded promontories. Beach deposits consist of calcareous sand from the reefs which fringe the islands, lava pebbles, and various minerals associated with lava.

II

LANDSCAPE FEATURES

23 | Rock Types and Structures

The configuration of a specific landscape feature carved by the forces of gradation is primarily determined by the type of rock which is being weathered and by its structure.

ROCK TYPES

The three major categories of rocks are associated with the three major geologic processes. Igneous rocks result from the cooling and solidification of hot liquid rock—magma or lava; sedimentary rocks are produced by the consolidation of sediments which have been formed by weathering and piled up by one of the agents of erosion; metamorphic rocks result from the modification of either sedimentary or igneous rock by pressure, heat, or hot solutions, all associated generally with times of mountain building.

The colors of igneous rocks are the result of the color of the preponderant mineral(s) composing the rock, except in the case of igneous rock glass, which is not composed of minerals. A mineral is a naturally occurring chemical compound with a distinguishing set of properties (hardness, color, cleavage, etc.) The black tone to basalt and gabbro is due to the presence of black-colored minerals (amphiboles, pyroxenes, calcium-rich feldspar). The dark color reflects the different chemical com-

Common Igneous Rocks

Texture	Light colored	Dark colored
Very coarse grained	Granite pegmatite	
Coarse granular (separate mineral grains very obvious)	Granite	Gabbro
Fine granular (generally need a microscope to see individual grains)	Rhyolite and andesite	Basalt
Dense glass	Obsidian	
Frothy glass	Pumice	Scoria

position of these rocks from the light-colored (reddish and various shades of light gray) granite, granite pegmatite, rhyolite, and andesite. The dark-colored rocks have a somewhat larger percentage of iron and magnesium and a lower percentage of potassium and silica than do the light-colored rocks. Although obsidian is generally black, it has the same chemical composition as the light-colored rocks.

The texture of an igneous rock varies according to the environment in which it solidified. A very quick freezing at the earth's surface results in a glassy texture. An abundance of dissolved gases in the lava gives a frothy or porous texture, such as that of pumice or scoria.

Moderately rapid cooling at the surface or in small intrusives near the surface produces a fine texture.

Coarse textures come about by the slow growth of individual mineral grains to a large size, such as occurs when magma cools very gradually deep down in the crust. Coarseness may also be due to the growth of minerals in a vein by the slow addition of material carried in solution.

At times, a mass of magma starts to cool slowly at depth, and then, before solidification is complete, it may be extruded through the earth's surface or intruded between cool rocks. This history results in a porphyritic texture, in which two sizes of mineral grains are present: a group of larger ones (phenocrysts) embedded in a finer-grained groundmass.

Granite is the most common intrusive rock (cooled and solidified at depth), and basalt the most common extrusive (cooled at the earth's surface). Granite pegmatites occur as veins which cut across previously formed rocks. In pegmatites, the individual mineral grains may reach many feet in length, but more commonly they vary from a fraction of an inch to a few inches across. These mineral grains are commonly quartz, mica, and feldspar.

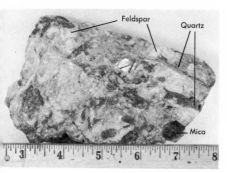

FIG. 23–1.

GRANITE PEGMATITE. The quartz has a glassy luster and is slightly darker in tone than the feldspar. Mica can be readily separated into thin flakes and is easily scratched with a knife.

FIG. 23–2.
GRANITE.

FIG. 23–3.
OBSIDIAN. Specimen shows typical conchoidal fracture.

FIG. 23–4.
GABBRO.

FIG. 23–5.
BASALT. Dike cutting granite.

FIG. 23–6.
BASALT PORPHYRY. Note the large feldspar phenocrysts.

Feldspar

FIG. 23–7.
SCORIA.

Common Sedimentary Rocks

Sediment	Sedimentary Rock
Mud	Shale
Sand	Sandstone
Gravel	Conglomerate
Lime, mud, and shell fragments	Limestone

The most noticeable feature of sedimentary rocks is their layering, which is obvious because of differences between layers in such characteristics as resistance to weathering and variations in color and grain size.

Shales, which underlie slopes and valleys, are generally weak compared with the other sedimentary rocks, while sandstones and conglomerates are resistant and protrude as ridges and cliffs. Limestone is resistant in comparison with shale, especially in arid areas, and is often a prominent cliff-maker there. In humid areas, because of its solubility, it is more apt to be found in valleys.

A sedimentary rock may preserve any features or objects found in connection with a sediment, such as shells, bones, footprints (fossils), ripple marks, and mud cracks.

The colors of sedimentary rocks vary widely. Limestone is white when pure, and sandstone is white when composed of unstained quartz grains. Most shades of gray to black are due to the presence of carbon from organic debris, such as in black shale and black limestone. Various shades of red are due to hematite (iron oxide), and yellow-browns to limonite (hydrous iron oxide).

FIG. 23–8.
SHALE. Note how this black shale has broken into a flat slablike piece.

FIG. 23–9.
SANDSTONE. This shows color banding.

FIG. 23–10.
CONGLOMERATE. Note that the large pebble is composed of rounded rock and mineral fragments. Such a rock is sometimes called pudding stone.

FIG. 23–11.

SHALE AND SANDSTONE SLOPE. Sandstone is typically more resistant than shale and outcrops here along the steeper parts of the slope.

Above:
FIG. 23–12.
FOSSIL SHELLS IN SANDSTONE.

Right:
FIG. 23–13.
RIPPLE MARKS IN SANDSTONE.

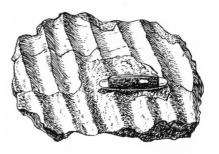

Common Metamorphic Rocks

Antecedent Rock	*Metamorphic Rock*
Shale	Slate
Sandstone	Quartzite
Limestone	Marble
Some igneous or sedimentary rock	Schist
Some igneous or sedimentary rock	Gneiss

Metamorphic rocks are formed from any preexisting sedimentary or igneous rocks under conditions of high temperature, high pressure, and chemically active solutions. They are characteristically banded or layered in some fashion, often finely foliated. This structure shows up on individual rock outcrops and, on a larger scale, may extend for long distances across country.

Quartzite, schist, and gneiss are the metamorphic rocks generally the most resistant to weathering and erosion; slate and marble are less so.

Pure marble is white; variations in coloring reflect variations in amounts and kinds of impurities. Quartzite is white, if composed of pure quartz, but may be reddish or gray. Slate may be black, gray, or red. Schist and gneiss commonly show various shades of gray; on close inspection they can be seen to be composed of varying proportions of light- and dark-colored minerals.

FIG. 23–14.
SLATE. Note the fine lines of cleavage on the near end of the specimen.

FIG. 23–15.
QUARTZITE. The specimen shows faintly the typical glassy reflection of quartzite.

FIG. 23–16.
MARBLE. Note how light is reflected from the surfaces of some of the mineral grains.

FIG. 23–17.
SCHIST. Note the relatively fine foliation on the sides of the specimen, commonly due to the uniform orientation of platy flakes of mica.

FIG. 23–18.
GNEISS. Note the characteristic discontinuous bands, composed of alternating light- and dark-colored minerals.

Many rock surfaces do not show the true color of the fresh, unaltered rock, which is revealed only when the surface is broken away. Rocks containing iron-bearing minerals weather on the surface to a yellow-brown color. This surface stain is due to limonite, formed by the addition of oxygen and water from the atmosphere to iron from the rock. Red surface coatings are due to hematite, an iron oxide. Dark gray to black coatings on rocks near a city are often due to soot and various other atmospheric pollutants. Chocolate brown to black surface stains found on rocks in desert areas (desert varnish) are due to a coating of manganese and iron oxides.

ROCK STRUCTURES

Tilts and Folds: Layered rocks—that is, sedimentary, metamorphosed sediments, or lava flows—may be horizontal, tilted, or folded.

An essentially horizontal structure is widespread, appearing in plain and plateau areas. The sides of river valleys, especially in plateau country, will reveal in cross-section some of the layers, the more resistant of which will form cliffs, and the less resistant, slopes. When a slight tilt is present, a more resistant layer will, on erosion, form an asymmetric ridge or cuesta.

In many mountain areas there are folded sediments which, when eroded, will produce a ridge-and-valley type of landscape.

An eroded dome is commonly rimmed by hogbacks if the dip of the layers is relatively steep, or by cuestas if the dip is gentle. The steep scarp face of the cuesta in such a case faces inward toward the center of the uplift. An eroded basin, on the other hand, will be encircled by a cuesta whose steep face points away from the center of the downwarp.

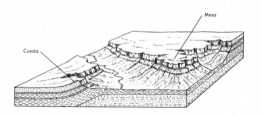

FIG. 23–19.

SIMPLE SEDIMENTARY ROCK STRUCTURES. Horizontal layers of sandstone and shale at the right have been eroded to form a mesa with a caprock layer of sandstone. At the left the structure is tilted. Erosion has produced an asymmetric ridge (cuesta), the resistant layer again being sandstone.

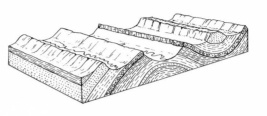

FIG. 23–20.

FOLDED SEDIMENTS. Note that the ridges are composed of conglomerate or sandstone and that the valleys are cut into shale.

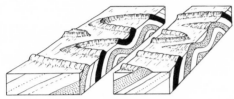

FIG. 23–21.

ERODED PLUNGING FOLDS. Such a structure is typical of the Ridge and Valley province of the Appalachian Mountains.

FIG. 23–22.

ERODED DOME. Black Hills, South Dakota. Note rimming hogback ridges (steep dips) and cuestas (gentle dips). The steepest sides of the asymmetric cuesta ridges face toward the center of the dome.

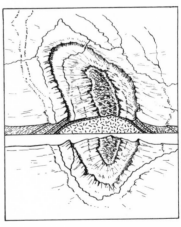

FIG. 23–23.

ERODED BASIN. Note that the steep sides of the cuestas face away from the center of the basin.

Joints: All rocks, whatever their origin, are jointed. A joint is a fracture in a rock along which there has been no visible relative motion of one side compared with the other.

Joints characteristically appear in sets, that is, in groups roughly parallel to each other. Spacing may be from a fraction of an inch to over a 100 feet, commonly a foot or so. A set of joints may intersect with another, thus "blocking out" solid rock by planes of weakness.

FIG. 23–24.
JOINTED HORIZONTAL SED-
IMENTS. Ausable Chasm, New
York.

FIG. 23–25.
JOINTED GRANITE. Dedham,
Massachusetts. Road cut.

Faults: A fracture where the rock on one side has slipped with respect to that on the other is a fault. There are three major types of faults. Normal faults, where the rock overlying the fault plane has slipped downward with respect to that underneath, are characteristic of fault-block mountains. Thrust faults, associated with folded mountains, occur where one part of the crust is pushed up and over another part; they are common in the Folded Appalachian Mountains and the Northern Rockies. In the strike-slip fault (so-called because the motion is parallel to the strike, i.e., trend, of the fault plane), slippage is essentially horizontal. The San Andreas Fault of California is a classic example of this.

Both joints and faults form planes of weakness which permit weathering agents to penetrate into a solid rock mass and thus control the location of valleys and also the configuration of cliff faces.

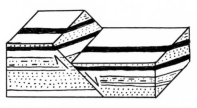

FIG. 23–26.
NORMAL FAULT. This is typical in fault-block mountains.

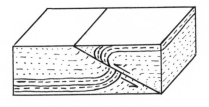

FIG. 23–27.
THRUST FAULT. This is commonly associated with folded rocks. Note how the layers have been bent in connection with the fault motion.

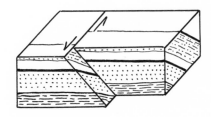

FIG. 23–28.
STRIKE-SLIP FAULT. Motion along the fault plane is horizontal.

24 | Igneous Rock Landscapes

Igneous activity is responsible for the production of a set of very characteristic landscape features. The piling up of volcanic debris at the earth's surface produces flows and cones with a great variety of sizes and shapes, and igneous activity of long ago may control present-day landscapes when erosion uncovers various types of intrusive igneous rock bodies. Since such bodies will, in general, have a different resistance to erosion than the rocks around them, they will protrude as hills and ridges if harder; or, more rarely, if they are less resistant, form hollows and small valleys.

Cones: Volcanic cones, formed of material piled up around a vent, may be composed of volcanic fragments, alternating layers of fragments and lava, or primarily of lava.

FIG. 24–I.

SPATTER CONES. Craters of the Moon National Monument, Idaho. These are built of spattering gouts of sticky basaltic lava emitted spasmodically from a vent. Typically, they are steep sided and are generally less than 50 feet high.

Left:

FIG. 24–2.

CINDER CONE. Amboy Crater, California. Such features are composed of cinders, volcanic bombs, and blocks of hardened rock, which have emerged explosively from a central vent to build edifices a few hundreds of feet high. Slopes are steep and rubbly.

Right:

FIG. 24–3.

STRATO-VOLCANO. Mount Saint Helens, Washington. This shape is typical of the classic large volcanoes of the world, such as Mounts Hood, Rainier, and Fuji. Composed of alternating layers of ash and lava, this cone, thousands of feet high, takes thousands of years to produce. The flanks may be embellished with cinder cones, and there may be fields of pumice fragments produced at times of explosive eruption.

5 MILES

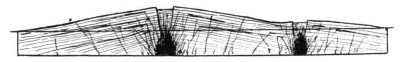

FIG. 24–4.

SHIELD VOLCANO. Sectional view of Mauna Loa and Kilauea, Hawaii. Such enormous rounded cones, which are much broader than they are high, are formed essentially of liquid lava combined with a relatively small amount of explosive activity necessary to give ash and cinders. Note the large collapse depression, or caldera, at the summit of each.

FIG. 24–5.

CALDERA. Crater Lake, Oregon. A number of volcanoes have a crater at the top much larger than the volcanic vent. Such a feature, which may be a number of miles across, is primarily the result of collapse following the retreat of lava back into the throat of the cone.

FIG. 24–6.

VOLCANIC BOMBS. These porous chunks of lava, which vary in size from a few inches to a number of feet, form when liquid masses of lava are violently emitted from a cone and then harden in flight into various streamlined shapes.

Flows: Many lava flows, instead of erupting from a central vent and thus building up a cone, emerge along extensive fracture systems and flood out over a large area, such as those in the Columbia Plateau province. These flows, as well as those connected with a volcano, have a variety of structures and surface features. If of recent origin, they very often present a black desolation of ash, cinders, porous blocks, and mounds of debris.

Aa lava flows are characterized by a rough, irregular surface, formed when the lava crusted over and the underlying, still-liquid material continued to move, thus breaking up the overlying, solidified lava into angular blocks. Pahoehoe lava, in contrast, was more viscous immediately preceding solidification and thus shows a billowy, ropy surface.

Lava caves, which may vary in size from small lava tubes an inch or so in diameter to caverns tens of feet high and hundreds of feet long, form when lava drains away from under a hardened crust. Collapse of the surface into a cave explains some of the depressions found on a flow.

Active volcanic areas possess a number of features which are associated with recent flows or with the near approach of a mass of magma to the surface. *Fumeroles* are holes from which various volcanic gases escape; hot springs and geysers appear where rocks are hot at a relatively shallow depth. Rain water percolates underground, is heated, and then emerges quietly as a hot spring or, spasmodically, as a geyser.

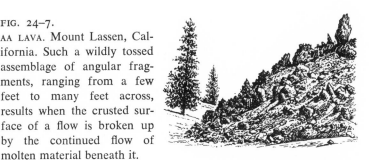

FIG. 24–7.
AA LAVA. Mount Lassen, California. Such a wildly tossed assemblage of angular fragments, ranging from a few feet to many feet across, results when the crusted surface of a flow is broken up by the continued flow of molten material beneath it.

FIG. 24–8.
PAHOEHOE LAVA. Craters of the Moon National Monument, Idaho. This flow consists of a ropy, twisted, and pleated mass of lava, often resembling pulled taffy.

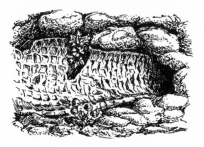

FIG. 24–9.

TREE MOLD. Craters of the Moon National Monument, Idaho. The hollows are produced when lava flows around branches and trunks of trees. Later, after the solidification of the lava, the tree may be completely burned or rotted away. The molds often show a checkerboard pattern on the inside reflecting the charred-wood pattern.

FIG. 24–10.

COLUMNAR JOINTING. Devil's Postpile, California. Such jointing is one of the most notable characteristics of many basalt flows. The formation of polygonal columns is due to contraction on cooling. Dikes and sills may also show this jointing. For the production of such a structure, the lava must not move after it starts to harden.

Intrusives: Intrusive igneous rock bodies are exposed at the surface when the overlying rock into which they were intruded is removed by weathering and erosion.

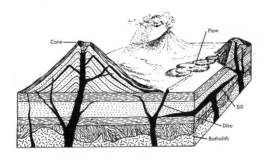

FIG. 24–11.

IGNEOUS ROCK FORMS. Note that deep and extensive erosion must occur for a batholith to be exposed at the surface. Batholiths appear as extensive areas of granite, which are many square miles in extent. Examples are the Idaho and Boulder Batholiths of the Northern Rockies.

Left:
FIG. 24–12.

DIKE. Cohasset, Massachusetts. This is basalt cutting granite. Such tabular, igneous rock bodies cut across preexisting material into which they are intruded. They may vary in size from less than an inch across to hundreds of feet. They are obvious in the landscape because they generally differ in color and texture from the surrounding rock and weather at a different rate.

Right:
FIG. 24–13.

SILL. Palisades, New York. This is a tabular body resembling a buried lava flow. It was intruded between preexisting layers of rock, which were pushed apart to make room. Sills vary in thickness from a few feet to hundreds of feet. The erosion of either a sill or a buried lava flow, which has been tilted, may produce an asymmetric ridge, with a gentle dip slope and a steep scarp face. The scarp face of the Palisades is shown here. Note the large-scale columnar jointing. The contact with the sediments under the sill is buried under the debris, which forms the slope in the foreground, and the overlying sediments have been entirely removed at this place.

FIG. 24–14.

VOLCANIC NECK. Shiprock, New Mexico. A volcanic neck is an isolated column of solidified lava filling the vent up which lava came to produce a presumed volcano, now entirely removed by erosion. It may commonly have radiating dikes, as is the case here.

AREAS OF IGNEOUS ROCK IN THE UNITED STATES.

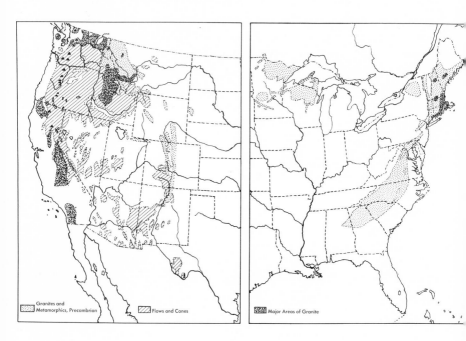

25 | Glaciated Landscapes

There are two major categories of glaciers: ice streams (valley glaciers) and ice sheets (continental glaciers and ice caps). Each type leaves a characteristic set of both erosional and depositional landforms. The most obvious erosional features are connected with ice streams, and the most widespread and obvious depositional features with ice sheets.

Glacial deposits, collectively, are called glacial drift. When laid down directly from melting ice, the debris is unsorted and is called till. In contrast, during transportation and deposition by streams of meltwater, the debris is sorted, at least to some extent, by size, the mud being separated from the sand, and this in turn from the gravel.

Lake basins are often formed in connection with glaciers, owing their origin to both the erosional and the depositional aspects of glaciation.

Ice Streams—Erosional Features: The erosional features associated with valley glaciers are very obvious and often visible from a distance of many miles. A glaciated mountain range characteristically has jagged peaks (horns), sharp ridges (arêtes), and deep amphitheater-shaped valley heads (cirques) on the mountain flanks.

Ice streams are confined to valleys, which they tend to

straighten, widen, and deepen. When the ice disappears, a valley with a U-shaped cross profile is left. Where drowned by a relative rise in sea level, U-shaped valleys form fjords in their seaward extremities.

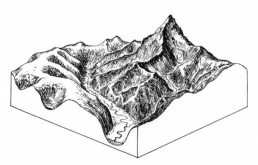

FIG. 25–1.

MOUNTAIN GLACIAL FEATURES. Note that the divides between cirque basins on the higher peak have been reduced to a sharp edge, whereas at the lower elevations, shown at the left, the divides are still rounded and show parts of the preglacial topography. The major U-shaped valley has been partially filled in by stream deposits made after the ice left.

FIG. 25–2.
U-SHAPED VALLEY. Crawford Notch, New Hampshire.

FIG. 25–3.
FINGER LAKES. Map of central New York State. Such lakes fill sections of U-shaped valleys which have been either gouged out more in one part than another or damned up by glacial debris.

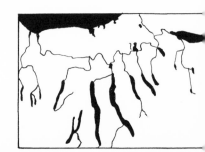

FIG. 25–4.

HANGING VALLEY. Bridalveil Fall, Yosemite National Park, California. Tributary ice streams will, in general, not erode their channels as rapidly as the major ice stream. Thus when the ice eventually disappears, hanging valleys and accompanying waterfalls will be left.

FIG. 25–5.

CIRQUE. King Ravine, White Mountains, New Hampshire. A glacier gouges out such amphitheater-shaped hollows by freezing onto frost-shattered blocks of rock and then carrying them away.

Left:
FIG. 25–6.
TARNS AND CIRQUES. Wind River Mountains, Wyoming. The floor of a cirque may be scooped out so as to leave a small rock basin in which a lake forms.

Right:
FIG. 25–7.
HORNS AND ARÊTES. Saint Elias Range, Alaska. The development and enlargement of a system of U-shaped valleys and cirques will eventually dissect a mountain mass to such an extent that only jagged peaks (horns) and sharp divides (arêtes) are left. Note also the medial moraines on the surface of the ice in the foreground.

Ice Streams—Depositional Features: The depositional features of valley glaciers, which are much less obvious than the erosional ones, consist most noticeably of moraines.

Medial moraines can be noted on the surface of present-day glaciers as dark lines of debris riding on the surface or embedded in the ice. They form when two ice streams join, thus bringing to the center of the glacier material which has fallen down the steep sides of the tributary valleys and has been at first carried along at the side of the tributary glaciers. They are especially obvious in some of the Alaskan glaciers.

Lateral moraines form on the sides of a valley glacier; they are most obvious in places where the glacier has reached the base of a steep slope and has spread out somewhat.

The terminus of an ice stream is marked by a terminal moraine. Such a deposit, however, is not apt to last very long because it is quickly removed by meltwater from the glacier.

Ice Sheets—Erosional Features: Unlike valley glaciers, ice sheets override hills and valleys alike. They erode the hills, producing smoothed rock ledges with striations and grooves, and fill in the lowland areas with deposits, thus tending to decrease the preglacial relief of a region. This is quite the reverse of valley glaciers, which emphasize the relief by eroding preglacial valleys still deeper.

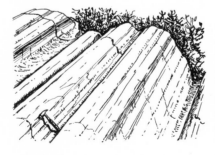

FIG. 25–8.
STRIATIONS AND GROOVES. Kelly's Island, Lake Erie. These are formed by the abrasive action of ice-borne boulders. When the ice load is composed of fine material, rock ledges may be given a polish.

FIG. 25–9.

ROCHE MOUTONNÉE. Kern Valley, California. Such a rock ledge is smoothed and given a streamlined shape by the passing of a mass of ice. Characteristically, it is asymmetrical in profile, being steeper on the lee side from which the ice has plucked rock fragments loosened by frost wedging. Such features vary from a very few feet to hundreds of feet across. Their surfaces often show deep grooves and striations. These are found in connection with valley glaciers also.

Ice Sheets—Depositional Features of Till: Glacial till is deposited directly from the ice as it melts; it is thus composed of whatever the ice had been carrying: mud, sand, and gravel, all mixed together in varying proportions. The proportions of these ingredients depend on the composition of the soil and bedrock over which the ice advanced.

Moraines are hummocky piles of till. Ground moraine is relatively thin and covers large areas. It is deposited by the ice as it retreats. Terminal (end) moraines, which are ridges a few tens to hundreds of feet high, extend for miles and were deposited when the glacial front remained relatively stationary for some time; i.e., ice advance kept approximate pace with the rate at which the front melted back. The width of such moraines varies from hundreds of feet to a mile or more, depending on how steady the front of the ice was. Interlobate moraines are deposited between lobes (tongues) of two masses of ice.

Erratics, or glacier-borne boulders, are often found embedded in the till or, in places, perched on rock ledges.

Where the ice has overridden piles of till, it has shaped the till into an oval, streamlined hill, or drumlin.

FIG. 25–10.
MORAINAL TOPOGRAPHY.
Prince William Sound, Alaska.

FIG. 25–11.
MORAINAL TOPOGRAPHY. Cuyler, New York. The hollows are kettle holes, that is, collapse depressions formed when a buried block of ice melted.

FIG. 25–12.
DRUMLIN. Wayne County, New York. This oval hill of till is elongated in the direction of ice motion, being slightly steeper on the side from which the ice came. Drumlin dimensions vary from 50 to over 100 feet high and from one quarter to over a mile in length.

FIG. 25-13.

ERRATIC. Central Park, New York City, New York. Such glacier-borne boulders appear in till deposits or perched on rock ledges. They are often composed of rock unlike that native to the region in which they are found.

Ice Sheets—Meltwater Deposits: Deposits laid down by melt-waters from now-vanished glaciers are extensive in the northern parts of the United States. Such glacio-fluviatile deposits are always sorted to some extent, the finer particles being separated from the coarser. Depending on the environment of deposi-tions they appear in a variety of shapes and sizes, such as outwash plains, lake deposits, kames and eskers.

An outwash plain, which is a gently sloping deposit of strati-fied layers of sand and gravel, is laid down by water streaming away from the front of a glacier. The south side of Long Island affords an excellent example.

Lakes which were formerly dammed by masses of ice were the dumping ground for debris. They may now be drained and appear as stretches of very flat country, floored by layers of mud and sand.

FIG. 25–14.

ESKER. Pine River, New Hampshire. Such deposits often extend for thousands of feet to a number of miles, characteristically through swampy country. They vary in height from 10 to 100 feet or so and are composed of roughly sorted sand and gravel layers, which were laid down by a stream flowing under the ice or in a crevasse.

FIG. 25–15.

KAME. Kettle Moraine State Forest, Wisconsin. This conical hill of roughly sorted debris was laid down by glacial meltwaters in a hole in the ice or as a small fan-shaped deposit at the edge of a stagnating mass of ice.

FIG. 25–16.

KETTLE HOLE. Cape Cod, Massachusetts. Such a bowl-shaped depression in till or outwash was formed when a buried block of ice melted.

Areas of Permafrost: Regions where the ground is permanently frozen at depth and where there is melting downward from the surface in the summer have distinctive types of landforms. These are found in northern Alaska and Canada and elsewhere at high elevations.

Thaw (thermokarst) lakes develop in the summer months, when the insulating layer of vegetation is broken through and the upper part of the permafrost layer (up to 50 per cent water by volume) is exposed to melting temperatures. The soil collapses into such a lake, which then grows by the melting of the permafrost on the banks. A series of connected lake basins develops into a beaded pattern of lakes.

FIG. 25–17.

SOLIFLUCTION LOBES. Seward Peninsula, Alaska. Water-saturated soil debris overlying permanently frozen ground has oozed downhill here under the force of gravity. This may occur on slopes as low as 2 degrees.

FIG. 25–18.

STONE POLYGONS. Clearwater Mountains, Alaska. The coarser material in a soil, the pebbles and boulders, has been separated from the finer clay by a sequence of freeze-and-thaw cycles. The sorting action results because silt and clay absorb more moisture than the coarser materials and, on freezing, push the gravel outward, away from the patches of clay. On thawing, the clay contracts, and the coarse material remains where it was pushed. Another freeze enables the clay to push the boulders yet further away. When such sorting action occurs on a slope, the polygons are drawn out by downhill creep into stone stripes.

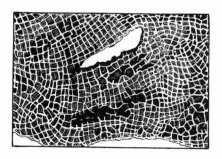

FIG. 25–19.

ICE-WEDGE POLYGONS. Arctic Coastal Plain, Alaska. These features develop where the growth of vertical wedges of ice in a polygonal pattern has thrust aside surface debris into low mounds and ridges. The ice is marked by low troughs. Polygons shown are 50 to 100 feet across.

FIG. 25–20.

PINGO. Arctic Coastal Plain, Alaska. This is a low rounded mound of turf that was pushed up by ice pressure from beneath. Pingoes occur when water, trapped under high pressure between permafrost at depth and confining soil layer above, breaks through to quickly freeze into a blister of ice under the surface layer of vegetation. They may extend to 200 to 300 feet high.

AREAS OF GLACIAL FEATURES IN THE UNITED STATES.

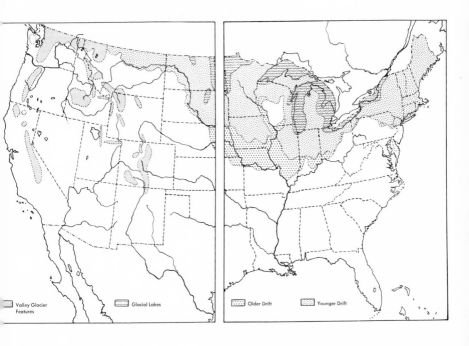

Valley Glacier Features   Glacial Lakes   Older Drift   Younger Drift

26 | *River Features*

Water running off the land is the most powerful and important of all erosional agents. It is responsible for the fashioning of the most obvious landscape feature: the valleys and the intervening hills and ridges. The latter, in most cases, are unremoved remnants of soil and rock left behind as the valleys between them were carved out by stream action.

Valleys vary in size from a small gully indenting a hillside and cut by a single rainstorm to the Grand Canyon with its raging torrent at the bottom of a precipitously walled valley a mile deep to the wide, flat valley of the slow-moving, meandering Mississippi.

The cutting of any valley involves two geologic functions of flowing water: First, a stream acts as a transportation agent to remove debris (mineral and rock fragments) brought to it; second, the larger particles in transit act as abrasive tools to scour the bedrock of the channel and thus slowly to deepen it. The valley, above the reach of the stream, is widened by the weathering of the rock and the subsequent falling, sliding, or washing of this loosened debris downslope to the river, which promptly carries it away.

Stream Patterns: Patterns of streams and their valleys as shown on a map or seen from the air vary widely from place to place because of variations in rock structure and geologic history.

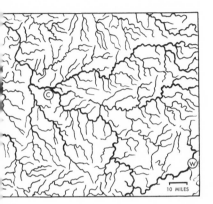 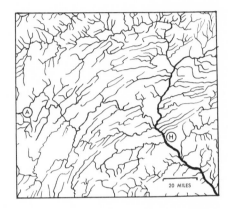

Left:

FIG. 26–1.

DENDRITIC PATTERN. West Virginia. (C—Charleston, W—White Sulphur Springs.) This pattern is characteristic of plains and plateaus where the horizontal layers of rock do not exert any control over the location of stream valleys; that is, streams flowing in one area do not find it any easier or harder to cut downward than streams flowing elsewhere. All scales are found, ranging from the Missisippi River system to a channel system developed on a pile of dirt after a heavy rain. Tributaries characteristically join the next larger channel, so that the acute angle of junction points upstream.

Right:

FIG. 26–2.

TRELLIS PATTERN. Pennsylvania. (A—Altoona, H—Harrisburg.) This pattern, characteristic of folded rocks, shows a strong control by the rock structure over the development of valleys. There has been a selective etching of valleys along weak rock belts and the leaving of the more resistant belts as ridges between the valleys. Plunging folds show up as a series of nonparallel valleys and ridges, which may converge to form S-shaped ridge-and-valley systems.

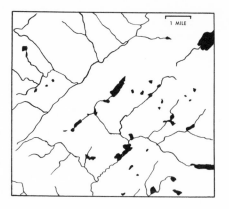

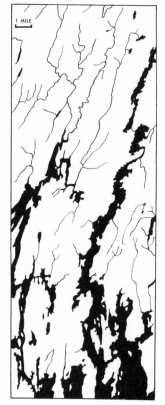

Above:

FIG. 26–3.

RECTANGULAR PATTERN. Elizabethtown Quadrangle, Adirondack Mountains, New York. This pattern develops where a series of faults or a well-developed joint system controls the places and directions of valley cutting. It may be combined with the dendritic pattern as it is at the Grand Canyon in Arizona where cliff faces and stream intersections show some angularity.

Left:

FIG. 26–4.

CONTORTED PATTERN. Boothbay Quadrangle, Maine. This pattern, consisting of roughly parallel stream valleys, is found in areas of metamorphic rocks where alternating weak and resistant bands control the location of valleys and ridges. The control does not appear as straight or as continuous as in folded sedimentary sequences. The seaward ends of the valleys have been drowned here.

Left:

FIG. 26–5.

FAULT-CONTROLLED PATTERN. San Andreas Fault, Point Reyes area, California. A fault forms a line of weakness, thus determining the location of valley cutting. Tomales Bay, the deep estuary at the top of the map, Bolinas Bay below the middle, and the valley joining them follow the fault zone, which trends northwest-southeast.

Below:

FIG. 26–6.

PARALLEL PATTERN. Mesa Verde, Colorado. A series of streams all flowing in the same direction is found on coastal plains, uplifted and drained lake floors, and tilted mesas, as here, where the slope of the land causes the major streams to be roughly parallel. An individual stream and its tributaries may appear dendritic in form.

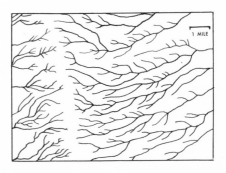

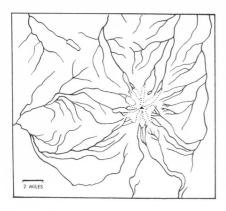

FIG. 26–7.

RADIAL PATTERN—OUTWARD FLOW-ING. Mount Hood, Oregon. A pattern of streams that radiate from a central point is commonly associated with a volcanic cone.

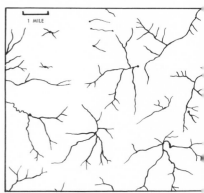

FIG. 26–8.

RADIAL PATTERN—INWARD FLOW-ING. Standingstone Quadrangle, Tennessee. Streams here converge into sinkholes, the water continuing its journey via underground passageways.

Valley Profiles:

FIG. 26–9.

V-SHAPED VALLEY (CLASSIC SHAPE). Yellowstone Canyon, Wyoming. This is characteristic of a youthful stream or one in which the river is actively scouring out its bed. The stream fills in the very bottom of the V and the sides flare upwards and away from each other. Rocks here are of uniform resistance to erosion.

FIG. 26–10.
V-SHAPED VALLEY (STEEP-WALLED). Oneonto Gorge, Oregon. Wherever the weathering and crumbling away of the valley sides is slow compared with the rate of downcutting by the river, the walls may be essentially vertical for some distance upwards.

FIG. 26–11.

V-SHAPED VALLEY (STEEP WALLS). Grand Canyon, Arizona. In plateau areas the classic V-shape of a youthful valley may be modified into steps, which are obviously the result of alternating layers of resistant and less resistant rock. The resistant layers form the cliffs, and the slopes are underlain by less resistant material.

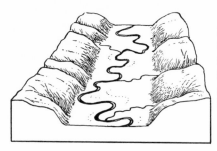

FIG. 26–12.
FLOOD-PLAIN VALLEY. The profile across a flood-plain river shows a flat floor bordered by rising land, often a zone of deeply dissected bluffs.

FIG. 26–13.
U-SHAPED VALLEY. Crawford Notch, New Hampshire. A river valley modified by glacial erosion shows such a cross profile.

FIG. 26–14.
U-SHAPED VALLEY WITH FLAT FLOOR. Yosemite Valley, California. Valleys which have been scoured out by a glacier and then partially filled in by later stream deposits show a flat alluvial floor above which the valley sides rise steeply. The angular junction between the floor and the sides is characteristically very abrupt.

Young Rivers: The typical youthful river valley is one which has a winding path, a V-shaped cross-profile, and a bedrock bottom for much of the way. Falls and rapids are common. In mountainous areas especially, the channel may have many pebbles and large boulders, some of which may be moved only at times of rare major floods. Along such a stream, rock ledges are apt to be rounded and smoothed by the abrasive action of sand and gravel in transit.

Falls and rapids occur at places where the river leaves more resistant rock to flow over less resistant materials. Plunge pools are often ground out at the base of waterfalls by the churning action of swirling water using boulder and gravel tools.

FIG. 26–15.
YOUNG RIVER. Note the many pebbles and boulders.

FIG. 26–16.
NIAGARA FALLS, NEW YORK. The Niagara River here drops from a resistant cap rock onto less-resistant, underlying layers.

FIG. 26–17.

FALLS OF THE POTOMAC RIVER, WASHINGTON, D.C. The river here leaves resistant rocks of the Piedmont province for softer rocks of the Coastal Plain province.

FIG. 26–18.
POTHOLES. Peabody River, New Hampshire. These features are similar in origin to plunge pools. They were drilled by boulder-and-gravel tools along rocky stretches of a boulder-laden stream.

FIG. 26–19.
ALLUVIAL FANS. Mojave Desert, California. Fans are deposited by streams at the foot of mountain slopes in arid regions. They resemble deltas in origin, in that in each case the carrying capacity of a stream comes to an end.

Flood-plain Rivers: Flood-plain river valleys represent a late stage in the development of a stream valley. The characteristics of a flood-plain river are strikingly different from those of a youthful stream. The cross-profile has a wide, flat bottom, the river generally being confined to a channel which meanders across the valley floor. At times of flood, the whole floor may be inundated.

A zone of bluffs, often highly dissected, usually borders a flood plain. From the air, a wide flood plain may present a bewildering maze of abandoned channels, oxbow lakes, point bars, and meandering tributaries.

The locations of the meanders of a river constantly shift through the years. A river, as it rounds a bend, undercuts the outer bank and deposits material on the inner bank, where the flow of the water is less rapid. Such point bars are crescent-shaped; a series of abandoned ones may form intricate patterns when seen from the air.

Periodically, at times of flood, a meander loop may be abandoned by the river as it takes a shorter and more direct course. Such an abandoned loop forms a crescent-shaped hollow, or oxbow lake, when filled with water.

The channel of a meandering river may be bordered by a low ridge of sand and gravel—a natural levee—deposited at times of flood when a rapidly moving stream first overtops its banks. When this happens, the rate of flow is suddenly lessened and the coarser material dumped, while the river with its load of finer mud particles may spread over the whole flood plain.

FIG. 26–20.
MEANDERS. White River, Indiana. Note the oxbow lake.

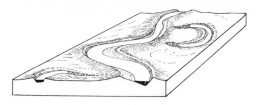

FIG. 26–21.

FEATURES OF A MEANDERING RIVER. Note the abandoned meander loop, now an oxbow lake, the point bars on the inside of the meanders, and the natural levee bordering the stream.

FIG. 26–22.

BRAIDED RIVER. Alaska. Some floodplain rivers, instead of having a single meandering channel, may have many small channels which diverge one from another and meet again in a very intricate way.

FIG. 26–23.
DELTA. Saint Clair River, Michigan. (D—Detroit.)

FIG. 26–24.
DELTA. Mississippi River. The area shown is approximately 150 miles west to east.

River Rejuvenation: An increase in the ability of a flood-plain river to carry its load, that is, rejuvenation, will result in the scouring out of its bed to a new and somewhat lower level. This may leave terraces of river deposits above the new level, which mark the former flood-plain level. Some rivers possess only one; others have a series of terraces, one above the other. The increased capability to carry material may be due to a climatic change or to a raising or tilting of the land.

If the capacity to erode is large enough, a meandering river may entirely cut through and remove its former flood-plain coating and incise itself into the underlying bedrock. Throughout this process the meandering path is maintained. Thus, such a history explains the meandering course of some youthful rivers. During the process of incision, a river may shift its path somewhat sideways as it cuts downward, with the result that the valley shows a much steeper slope on the outside of a bend (undercut slope) than on the inside of a bend (slip-off slope).

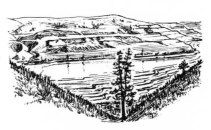

FIG. 26–25.
RIVER TERRACES. Columbia River, Washington.

FIG. 26–26.
INCISED MEANDERS. San Juan River, Utah. Slip-off and undercut slopes are not present here.

27 | Coastal Features

The largest scale feature to be noted along the coast is the trend of the shore itself. In places it is remarkably straight, but more usually it is irregular, and may be deeply indented by arms of the sea. A closer look at the coast reveals the fact that in some sections ocean waves and currents are wearing away the land, and in others the land is being extended as beaches and sand bars.

Shapes of Coastlines: The major shapes of coastlines as noted on maps, or from a vantage point such as an airplane, are explainable in terms of the shape of the land prior to a recent worldwide rise in sea level. Various agents of erosion, primarily streams, shaped the land, which was then inundated by the sea. The seaward ends of the valleys were flooded to form estuaries, intervalley areas became promontories, and hills became islands. Coastlines thus reflect the drainage pattern which existed before inundation.

Glacially shaped landscapes are responsible for the fjord coast of Alaska. The oval islands in Boston Harbor are drumlins, of which only the tops extend above water; the two eastward projections of Long Island—Orient Point at the north and Montauk Point at the south—mark the locations of two morainal ridges which continue below sea level beyond these points.

Where stream deposition has been more rapid than drowning and has kept up with the recent submergence, deltas have been formed.

FIG. 27–1.

CHESAPEAKE BAY. A river system with a dendritic pattern has been drowned here.

FIG. 27–2.

COAST OF MAINE. The area shown extends from Portland to Rockland. A contorted river pattern has been drowned here.

FIG. 27–3.
POINT REYES, CALIFORNIA. The drowning of a fault-controlled lowland explains the presence of the elongated Tomales Bay at the northwest and the Bolinas Bay towards the south.

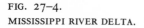

FIG. 27–4.
MISSISSIPPI RIVER DELTA.

Erosional Features: Along the edge of the land, waves and currents provide a powerful sculpturing force. Waves, with sand and gravel as tools, break up solid rock and remove it, leaving such features as cliffs, caves, arches, and sea stacks. Weaker materials, such as those less well cemented or with many fractures, will be removed more readily than the sounder material on either side. Irregularities, from a fraction of an inch to many feet across, are thus explainable. Along a rocky coast, for instance, a dike may be weaker than the rock it intruded and be eroded into a deep cleft by surging waves.

A rise of the land with respect to sea level leads to raised wave-cut cliffs, benches, and beaches. In places, a series of such wave-formed features may be seen one above the other on the slope of a precipitous coast. They are especially notable along stretches of the Pacific coastline of the United States. Such features, combined with the universal presence of drowned valleys, indicate clearly that the land has been both higher and lower with respect to sea level than it is now.

FIG. 27–5.
SEA CLIFF AND BEACH. Nauset Beach, Cape Cod, Massachusetts. The cliff, approximately 70 feet high, is cut into soft glacial material.

FIG. 27–6.
SEA CLIFF AND CAVE. Pismo Beach, California.

FIG. 27–7.
SEA CLIFF AND ARCHES. Santa Cruz, California.

FIG. 27–8.
SEA CLIFF, STACKS, AND RAISED TER-RACE. Harris Beach, Oregon.

FIG. 27–9.
MARINE TERRACES. Palos Verdes Hills, California.

Depositional Features: Wave and current action builds up deposits of sand and gravel into beach deposits of various shapes and locations. They are found along the shore as a projection into the water (sand spit), joining an island to the land (tombolo), at the mouth of a bay (bay-mouth bar), or offshore.

Beach deposits show a number of features to be associated with the environment of breaking waves and moving currents. For instance, if there is a prevailing direction from which waves hit the shore and currents move, there is often a pile-up of sand and gravel on the windward side of breakwaters, while there is a removal on the leeward side. Where material is constantly being shifted, there is sorting into various sizes, gravel being separated from sand. In some places the sorting is better or more obvious than in others; perhaps layers rich in dark, slightly denser sand grains may be separated from less dense, light-colored quartz sand.

A different kind of irregularity occurs along a beach where low mounds of material, often somewhat coarser than average, are separated by crescent-shaped troughs. The spacing of these beach cusps is usually in some tens of feet. They mark a sorting taking place at right angles to the beach, whereas the more common sorting of sand and gravel parallels the shoreline.

In places the sand surface shows ripple marks; breaking waves leave swash marks at their highest point of advance, while rill marks are formed as a returning wave washes around a pebble.

FIG. 27–10.
SAND SPIT. Poponesset Beach, Cape Cod, Massachusetts.

FIG. 27–11.
TOMBOLO. Morro Rock, California.

FIG. 27–12.
BAY-MOUTH BARS. Martha's Vineyard, Massachusetts. Note how the bars have cut off the estuaries to form lagoons.

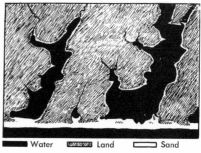

■ Water ▨ Land ▭ Sand

FIG. 27–13.
OFFSHORE BARS. Texas Coast. (C—Colorado River, B—Brazos River.) Note the estuaries formed by drowning behind the bars.

FIG. 27–14.
RIPPLE MARKS IN SAND.

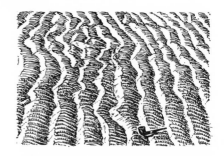

FIG. 27–15.
SWASH-AND-RILL MARKS. The swash marks roughly parallel the shore, and the rill marks extend downslope from pebbles.

FIG. 27–16.
BEACH CUSPS AND SWASH MARKS.

FIG. 27–17.
BEACH CUSPS IN GRAVEL.

Islands: Islands have a variety of origins. Most are merely hilltops of inundated land, such as those along the Maine Coast. Sea stacks, or erosional remnants, are generally smaller than drowned hills, lie closer to shore, and are clustered near a resistant headland. Sand bars lying offshore were formed by wave and current deposition. In tropical areas coral islands and reefs are found.

Volcanoes built up above sea level form several large and important groups of islands found widely distributed throughout the oceans of the world.

Any individual island, surrounded as it is by a very effective agent of erosion, is geologically a very transitory feature. Some disappear in a few years, and others in some thousands.

28 | Desert Forms

A desert environment is one of scant vegetation and long vistas uninterrupted by trees. River beds in these areas are generally dry, and dunes are built by the wind where there is a sufficient supply of sand. Alluvial fans and salt lakes, which vary in size and depth throughout the years, are characteristic features. Many desert areas have interior drainage; that is, whatever rain does fall never reaches the sea but evaporates, sinks into the ground, or flows into a temporary lake, where it eventually disappears by evaporation.

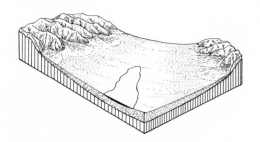

FIG. 28–1.

TYPICAL DESERT ENVIRONMENT. Note the alluvial fans at the base of the mountain slopes and the broad intermontane basin with the salt lake at the center.

Erosional Features: The etching and fashioning of bedrock surfaces into the great variety of weird shapes and forms found in a desert are due undoubtedly in some degree to sand blasting, but mostly to differential weathering; that is, to the breakup of certain less-well-cemented or consolidated parts of a rock at the expense of other parts. Material thus loosened is then blown or washed away.

Slopes in an arid region are especially susceptible to erosion by the rare rains, since loose material is not held in place by a vegetation cover.

The surface of an alluvial fan may often have a coating of closely fitting pebbles (desert pavement), which has been left behind when the finer dust and sand was carried farther by the wind. Here also may be found ventifacts, or wind-faceted pebbles, scoured and pitted by wind-driven sand.

FIG. 28–2.
DESERT EROSION. Form eroded in sandstone.

FIG. 28–3.
WATER-ERODED CLAY. Petrified Forest National Park, Holbrook, Arizona.

FIG. 28–4.
DESERT PAVEMENT. Death Valley, California.

FIG. 28–5.
VENTIFACTS. These pebbles were given their angular shape by sand blasting.

Depositional Features: Water-formed features of deserts consist primarily of alluvial fans and deposits laid down in a playa, or temporary lake.

Wherever there is a supply of loose sand, dunes are formed. A sufficient supply is found in only a small part of most deserts, in such places as alluvial fans, river beds, or where sandstone beds outcrop and are being weathered.

Dunes appear in a great variety of shapes and sizes, from a few feet to hundreds of feet high, covering areas from a few acres to many square miles.

Under conditions where there is a prevailing wind, dunes characteristically have a gentle side on the windward face, 5 to 15 degrees to the horizontal, and a steep lee side, 30 to 35 degrees. Such a dune is a moving one; sand is blown up the gentle slope and rolls down the lee side, the so-called slip face, to settle at the angle of repose of dry sand.

Dunes become fixed with a vegetation cover; removal of such a cover allows sand migration to begin again. The average dune may be quite irregular in outline, showing a number of blowouts, or parts where removal by the wind has been somewhat greater than elsewhere.

Crescent-shaped dunes (barchans) may develop under conditions of a prevailing wind direction and a limited supply of sand. The points of the crescent stream with the wind, and there are well-developed windward and slip faces.

Parabolic dunes resemble barchans in having a crescent shape, but in this case the points of the crescent face into the wind. The hollow between the points is a blowout, the points of the crescent being fixed. Barchans, parabolic dunes, and many others less regular in shape lie transversely to the wind. Under some conditions dunes develop parallel to the wind direction and belong to the category of longitudinal dunes.

Wind ripple marks are on many dunes. Their formation resembles that of the larger dune itself, being produced by the irregular deposition of moving sand.

FIG. 28–6.
ALLUVIAL FANS. Mojave Desert, California.

FIG. 28–7.
SAND DUNE. Note the gentle windward slope on the right and the steeper slip face on the left.

FIG. 28–8.
BARCHANS. Oregon. The wind direction was left to right.

FIG. 28–9.
RIPPLE MARKS ON A SAND DUNE.

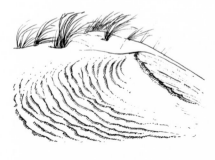

29 | Rock Sculpture: Shapes and Slopes

Most hills, ridges, cliffs, and slopes are erosional in origin; that is, they are remnants, the material from around, above, and to the side of them having been removed by the processes of weathering and erosion. Slopes not of such origin are of two types: recent fault scarps and slopes of deposition. The latter includes newly formed volcanic cones and flows and slopes associated with sedimentary deposits, such as sand dunes, alluvial fans, kames, and eskers.

The two characteristics which rocks possess that lead to most of the irregularities they show in their resistance to erosion are layering and fracturing. In bedded materials—that is, sedimentary rocks, the metamorphic equivalents of sedimentary rocks and lava flows—certain of the layers will inevitably be more resistant than others and stand out as steeper parts of a cliff face or as ridges, depending on whether the layers are horizontal or tilted. Fractures, whether joints or faults, produce weakened zones along which the rock breaks up more easily. Joints are present in all rocks as planes of weakness. In some places they are very close together, and in others, they may be a number of feet apart; they always, however, control to some extent the way in which rocks break away from a cliff face and, thus, the details of the face. In some rocks, layering and joint control are equally evident; in others, one or the other may be of paramount importance.

Varying resistances to weathering and erosion occur from the largest to the smallest scales, from a mountain peak to the bench-and-cliff arrangement of the walls of the Grand Canyon to the small, detailed irregularities which can be noted on all rock ledges. Such small-scale irregularities can be ascribed to a variety of causes, such as differences in resistance to weathering between separate mineral grains, varying degrees of cementation of mineral and rock particles, or minute bedding and fracture planes.

Wherever bedrock appears at the surface of the earth, the variations in erosional shapes reflect variations in resistance to breakup.

Ridges:

FIG. 29–1.
HOGBACKS. Front Range of the Rockies, Colorado. Tilted resistant layers protrude as ridges.

FIG. 29–2.
CUESTA. The Book Cliffs, Utah. Note the resistant cap overlying the weaker material which forms the slopes. The beds are tilted slightly towards the left.

FIG. 29–3.
ARÊTES. These jagged ridges are erosional forms which appeared as the cirques were eroded.

FIG. 29–4.
ROCHE MOUTONNÉE. Kern Valley, California. This is a glacially smoothed outcrop of rock.

Cliffs of Bedded Materials:

FIG. 29–5.
SANDSTONE-AND-SHALE CLIFF. Note how the more resistant sandstone forms the steepest parts of the cliff.

FIG. 29–6.
AUSABLE CHASM. New York. Two sets of vertical joints have blocked out these horizontal beds.

FIG. 29–7.
CROSSBEDDING. Canyon de Chelly, Arizona. The sandstone beds here show layering in an individual bed, forming an angle with the principal bedding planes, which are horizontal. Such a structure is associated with sand deposition in an environment where a layer is laid down and then partially eroded before another layer is deposited from a slightly different direction and inclination. Sand dunes and water-laid deposits both show this structure.

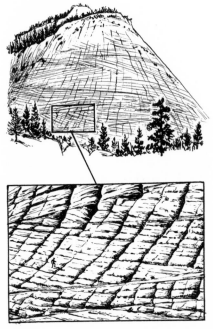

FIG. 29–8.
CHECKERBOARD MESA. Zion National Park, Utah. The sandstone here shows both crossbedding and jointing.

FIG. 29–9.
FOLDED ROCKS. Layers show variations in resistance to weathering.

FIG. 29–10.
LOESS CLIFF. Arizona. The cliff is approximately 8 feet high. Composed of wind-blown dust, loess has the capacity to stand up in cliffs, although very soft.

Cliffs of Granite:

FIG. 29–11.
JOINTING IN GRANITE. Massachusetts. Road cut.

FIG. 29–12.
OLD MAN OF THE MOUN-
TAIN, FRANCONIA NOTCH, NEW
HAMPSHIRE. The shape of this
weathered cliff-face was determined by the intersecting sets
of joints.

FIG. 29–13.
EL CAPITAN, YOSEMITE NA-
TIONAL PARK, CALIFORNIA.
The granite here has very few
joints, which are widely
spaced.

FIG. 29–14.
JOSHUA TREE NATIONAL MON-
UMENT, CALIFORNIA. The
granite blocks here were out-
lined by a system of joints and
then deeply weathered into
these rounded shapes.

FIG. 29–15.
SPHEROIDAL WEATHERING.
This block of granite has been
rounded by chemical weathering, which attacks the surface and leads to the spalling
off of concentric layers as
shown.

FIG. 29–16.
EXFOLIATION DOMES. Yosemite National Park, California. Such large domes of granite were formed by the peeling off of layers loosened by weathering.

FIG. 29–17.
EXFOLIATION. Summit of Half Dome, Yosemite National Park, California. The layers follow rounded joint cracks formed by the greater expansion of rock at the surface in comparison with that underneath.

FIG. 29–18.
GRANITE NEEDLES. Black Hills, South Dakota. In places granite with intersecting vertical joints may be weathered into a pinnacled landscape as shown.

Cliffs and Slopes in Weak Materials: Relatively weak sediments, such as clay, sand, and glacial deposits, do not stand up as cliffs on erosion but will form slopes, which may be furrowed by water-carved gullies.

FIG. 29–19.
SEACLIFFS. Nauset Beach, Cape Cod, Massachusetts. This cliff is cut into relatively soft glacial deposits.

FIG. 29–20.
CLAY SLOPES. Petrified Forest National Park, Arizona. Note how the slopes have been gullied by the rare rains.

FIG. 29–21.
BADLANDS. South Dakota. These horizontally bedded, soft and easily eroded deposits have been intricately dissected by water erosion.

Arches: Under special conditions a hole may be carved through a rock, giving an arch or natural bridge.

FIG. 29–22.

ANGEL ARCH, CANYONLANDS NATIONAL PARK, UTAH. This arch was formed by the selective removal of slightly weaker parts of the rock.

FIG. 29–23.

NATURAL BRIDGE. Virginia. This arch, composed of limestone, was left after the rocks on either side collapsed into a former subterranean river channel.

FIG. 29–24.

RAINBOW BRIDGE. Utah. This sandstone arch is 275 feet long and was cut by the river now floating under it. This river had a meandering course as it cut downward through the solid rock. Two of the meander loops approached each other to attack the separating spur of rock which, on being cut through, formed a bridge.

FIG. 29–25.
SEA ARCHES. California. Such
arches are cut by wave action.

Pillars: Isolated erosional remnants—pillars, pinnacles, and needles—have in detail a great variety of shapes, due to variations in rock type and structure.

Left:
FIG. 29–26.
MONUMENT VALLEY, ARIZONA. These erosional remnants of massive sandstone were left after the intervening parts of the layer were removed.

Right:
FIG. 29–27.
SANDSTONE PILLAR IN THE DESERT.

FIG. 29–28.
BRYCE CANYON NATIONAL
PARK, UTAH. These pillars
were carved from horizontal
sediments. A vertical system
of joints has led to the
erosional development of the
forms here.

FIG. 29–29.
PUMICE PINNACLES. Crater Lake National Park, Oregon. The separate pinnacles mark vents for volcanic gas which altered the pumice around them into a somewhat harder material than elsewhere.

FIG. 29–30.
CHIRICAHUA NATIONAL MONUMENT, ARIZONA. These mushroom-shaped erosional forms are formed of rhyolite.

Rockfalls, Slides, Slumps, and Soil Creep:

FIG. 29–31.
TALUS SLOPE. This slope of broken rock fragments lies at the base of a basalt cliff.

FIG. 29–32.
TALUS CONES. Madison Mountains, Montana. These cone-shaped piles of debris were concentrated down the steep gullies which extend farther upslope.

FIG. 29–33.
EARTH FLOW. Slumgullion Gulch, San Juan Mountains, Colorado.

FIG. 29–34.
LANDSLIDE. Gros Ventre Mountains, Wyoming. Note the obvious scar left by the slide.

FIG. 29–35.
EARTH SLUMP. Note the small terraces which have been formed and the bulging of the earth at the base.

FIG. 29–36.

SOIL CREEP. The diagram shows various types of evidence indicating soil creep. Trees planted on a slope sometimes show the lower parts of the trunks inclining downslope, with the upper parts vertical. Obviously the lower trunks grew vertically, but were bent by the slow downslope motion of the surface layers of soil.

30 | Limestone Caves and Ground Water

Ground water as a producer of landscape features is associated primarily with areas of limestone. This rock is readily soluble by rain as it percolates into the ground and may be so pitted and dissolved away that a special kind of topography, karst, results. This type of land has many sinkholes which pepper the surface, and caves are common. Drainage is largely underground. Rivers disappear into holes in the ground and reappear as springs, sometimes of very large volume.

Karst topography is best developed on massive limestone cut by a series of joints, along which solution occurs and openings are enlarged. An area of chalk, although also composed of calcium carbonate, does not develop sinkholes and caves to the extent of limestone, because chalk is highly permeable throughout its mass, not just along joint fractures.

FIG. 30–1.
KARST TOPOGRAPHY. The block diagram shows many sinkholes, disappearing streams, and a system of caves.

Caves: Cave openings in limestone vary in width from the microscopic to hundreds of feet and may extend for many miles. The changes in size of openings reflect changes in rock solubility as well as later differences in degree of filling. Constricted sections may either connect one cave with another on the same level or one level with another.

The shapes and arrangement of caves and passageways are determined by the bedding and the location and geometry of the system of joints.

Many caves are now being filled in by calcium carbonate deposits, called dripstone, as the result of a change in the level of the water table; that is, the level of saturated rock in the crust. The calcium carbonate is carried by percolating ground water, which picks it up nearer the surface and then precipitates it on reaching the cavern openings.

The fantastic variety in shape that cave deposits take is dependent in large measure on the arrangement of the cracks in the roofs of the caverns from which ground water emerges and the rate of flow. Most forms are variations on three basic shapes: the stalactite, or iciclelike form growing from the roof; the stalagmite, a more stumpy form growing upward from the floor; and the pillar or column, due to the coalescence of stalactite and stalagmite. Such forms, as well as the walls, may be embellished with pleats, wrinkles, folds, and a myriad other shapes. Pure calcium carbonate is white, but a great variety of colors is found due to small amounts of impurities deposited with the limestone. Floor deposits may include, in addition to the stalagmite, terrace growths and, where dripping water moves them, rounded calcite concretions called cave pearls. These are formed by precipitation around a small nucleus and often grow to one-half inch in diameter.

FIG. 30–2.
STALACTITES AND STALAG-
MITES. Mayfield Cave, Texas.

FIG. 30–3.
CAVE DEPOSITS. Leman Caves,
Nevada.

FIG. 30–4.
CAVE DEPOSITS. Luray Cav-
erns, Virginia.

FIG. 30–5.
PISOLITES. Carlsbad Caverns,
New Mexico. The "cave
pearls" shown here are about
a half inch in diameter.

Surface Deposits of Emerging Ground Water: Ground water may build up various deposits on emerging at the surface. Those associated with the hot springs of Yellowstone Park are notable. Calcium carbonate forms the deposits of travertine at Mammoth Hot Springs, and silica is deposited as the mineral geyserite around some of the geysers there.

FIG. 30–6.
MAMMOTH HOT SPRINGS, YEL-
LOWSTONE NATIONAL PARK.
This rock is formed of depos-
its of travertine.

31 | Lakes and Swamps

Any lake or swamp is geologically a very short-lived feature, which may exist for a few hundred years to at most some thousands, depending on original size and depth. It is the inevitable fate of any hollow on the land to be filled in with the deposits carried by entering streams, as well as by organic material growing along shallow margins. Furthermore, any stream which drains a lake tends to cut down its channel and thus lower the level of the lake. Thus, the widespread occurrence of lakes in many parts of the country calls for some explanation as to how hollows have been formed in the recent geologic past.

In any discussion of lakes, it is the origin of the basin which is important. Whether a lake is present or not is purely a matter of climate. In arid to semiarid regions, many of the hollows have no water in them. In humid areas, however, rainfall is generally sufficient for the bottom of most hollows to extend below the water table and thus to have standing water in them.

Swamps occur in areas which are poorly drained. They are associated with shallow lake margins being filled in with organic growth, with the last stages in the life of a lake which has been filled or drained, and in general, with any area of flat land where runoff is slow and sluggish. River flood plains and flat areas near the sea may possess extensive swamps.

Glacial Lakes: A comparison of a map of North America showing the distribution of lakes with one giving the extent of the recent ice sheet demonstrates a very close correlation. Quite obviously, ice on the land has been most effective in producing lake basins.

Rock-basin lakes were gouged out by the plucking action of moving ice, aided by the abrasion of entrapped boulders and sand dragged along by the glacier's motion. Such lake basins appear in many sizes, shapes, and locations. Small tarns lie in the deepened floors of many cirques. Greater gouging along parts of a glaciated valley may develop a series of hollows. When these are filled with water on the disappearance of the ice, they appear as a series of shining beads strung on a thread of flowing water.

Finger lakes fill larger sections of valleys, plowed out either by ice streams flowing down the sides of mountains or by tongues of ice extending down lowland areas in front of an ice sheet, as was the case in the formation of the Finger Lakes of New York State. Many lake basins in the Precambrian shield area of Canada have been formed by glacial scour, the depth of scour being greatest where rocks were less resistant, as along faults or joints. The rectangular shapes of the lakes and their linear arrangement in the Adirondack Mountains afford excellent examples of such control.

Glacial deposits produce lakes and swamps in a number of ways. Valleys may be dammed up by glacial debris. Kettle holes are found where an entombed block of ice has melted, thus causing the surface above it to collapse into a hollow. Kettles vary in size from a few feet across to an area covering many acres.

The partial melting of the ground in areas of permafrost results in so-called thermokarst lakes. These are found in parts of Alaska, especially on the Arctic Coastal Plain.

FIG. 31–1.
TARNS. Wind River Mountains, Wyoming. These lakes lie in the gouged-out floors of cirques.

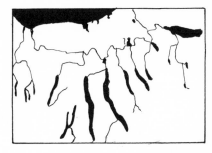

FIG. 31–2.
FINGER LAKES. Map of central New York State.

FIG. 31–3.
ARROWHEAD LAKE, ROCKY MOUNTAIN NATIONAL PARK, COLORADO. This is a glacially formed lake.

FIG. 31–4.
KETTLE POND. Cape Cod, Massachusetts.

Sink Holes:

FIG. 31–5.
SINKHOLES. Indiana. These occur as the result of solution by ground water in a limestone region. They may have water in them if they extend below the water table.

Flood-plain Lakes:

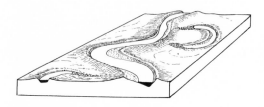

FIG. 31–6.
OXBOW LAKE. Such lakes develop on a flood-plain when a meander loop is abandoned by a shift in the river channel.

Lakes of Volcanic Origin: Hollows associated with igneous activity include craters and the much-larger calderas. Also, lava flows may dam up a stream channel, thus forming a lake basin.

FIG. 31–7.
CRATER LAKE. Oregon. This lake fills a caldera.

Lake Basins Associated with Mountain Building: Geologically recent warping and faulting of the earth's crust may lead to the formation of hollows in the land. The many large basins in the Basin and Range province are of such an origin. The scanty rainfall is enough to fill only the very bottom parts of a few of them. Such lakes may vary in extent and depth from season to season as there is often no outlet to the sea, and loss of water is only by evaporation. Examples include the Great Salt Lake in Utah, Pyramid Lake in Nevada, and Mono Lake in California.

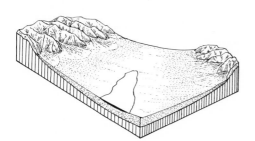

FIG. 31–8.
PLAYA LAKE. Such a lake may dry out entirely at times.

FIG. 31–9.
LAKE TERRACES. Lake Bonneville, Wasatch Mountains, Utah. These features were formed by the now-extinct Lake Bonneville. Great Salt Lake is a remnant of the former lake.

Artificial Lakes: The production of artificial lakes as the result either of excavation or of the damming up of streams is proceeding at an ever-increasing rate. They are especially obvious outside of the glaciated regions, where there were very few lakes before the work of man.

FIG. 31–10.
ARROWROCK DAM, IDAHO.

32 | Mountains

Most mountain peaks occur as members of a group of peaks in a range, all having a common structure and history. The great majority are erosional in origin; that is, they are relatively isolated remnants of an uplifted region formerly more extensive and less jagged. Volcanic cones are an exception, having been built by the accumulation of volcanic debris. However, they also will be attacked by the forces of weathering and erosion and quickly lose their original clean, conic shape.

A mountain range is such a large feature that the overall structure can best be appreciated from a map or perhaps from a plane high in the air.

The formation of a range may be the result of more-or-less straight uplift, faulting, doming, or folding.

Mountain ranges with the same origins often occur in groups to form mountain chains and systems. For instance, the large Basin and Range province of the United States is characterized by many fault-block mountains, and the Southern Rockies by many separate ranges of folded rocks.

Mountains are characteristically the home of swift, youthful streams, waterfalls, and rapids. Large boulders and coarse gravel often clog the channels and are moved only at times of flood. Steep slopes, cliffs, and landslide scars are present. Rockfalls have obviously occurred, which explain the large heaps of boulders (talus) found at the foot of cliffs.

The extremely rapid and deep erosion of mountains often uncovers material which at one time was buried far down in the crust. Thus, metamorphic rocks and granite are characteristically found in the cores of mountain ranges.

By far the most important agent of erosion in mountain carving is running water. Certain mountain areas, however, have been glaciated, with the result that the generally rounded contours of water-carved mountains have been sharpened to give steepened slopes, short, pointed peaks, and jagged divides.

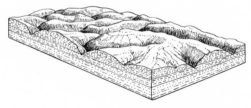

FIG. 32–1.

PLATEAU STRUCTURE. The layers were uplifted, and weathering and erosion primarily by streams has cut the valleys, leaving the hills as remnants.

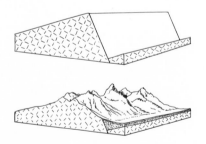

FIG. 32–2.

FAULT-BLOCK MOUNTAIN. The top diagram shows an uneroded block of the crust which was uplifted along a fault. The lower diagram shows it eroded into a number of peaks.

FIG. 32-3.
TRIANGULAR FACETS. Wasatch Mountains, Utah. This view of the west flank of the mountains shows the ridges between the valleys ending abruptly in triangular-shaped spur ends. They are essentially remnants of the fault plane along which the range was uplifted.

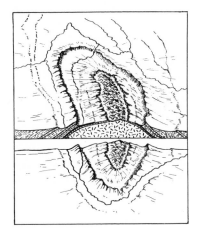

FIG. 32-4.
DOME. Black Hills, South Dakota. A core of granite has been exposed at the center. Hogbacks encircle the center.

FIG. 32-5.
FOLDED MOUNTAINS. The diagram shows the typical topography developed when a sequence of folded rocks is eroded.

FIG. 32-6.
CINDER CONE. Amboy Crater, California. This is a peak formed by the accumulation of cinders and ash.

Left:

FIG. 32–7.

STRATO-VOLCANO. Mount Saint Helens, Washington. This is a peak formed by the accumulation of lava and ash falls.

Right:

FIG. 32–8.

MOUNTAIN PEAKS, UNGLACIATED. Great Smoky Mountains National Park, Tennessee.

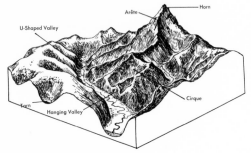

FIG. 32–9.

MOUNTAIN PEAKS, GLACIATED. The topography of glaciated mountains is far more jagged than that of unglaciated mountains.

FIG. 32–10.

MONADNOCKS. Moosehead Lake region, Maine. Such isolated peaks are the last remnants of an uplifted region which has been almost totally removed by weathering and erosion.

33 | Man and the Earth

Landscape features associated with the various activities of man are extensive and growing at an ever-increasing pace.

Road Patterns: Road patterns often reflect the topography of an area.

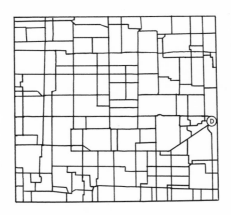

FIG. 33–I.

ROAD PATTERN, PLAINS. Iowa. (D—Fort Dodge.) Map area is 50 by 44 miles.

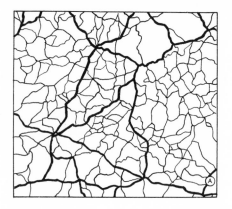

FIG. 33–2.
ROAD PATTERN, APPALACHIAN PLATEAU. Pennsylvania. (A—Altoona.) Map area is 50 by 44 miles. Most of the roads follow valleys or the height of land between valleys.

FIG. 33–3.
ROAD PATTERN, FOLDED ROCK. Pennsylvania. (H—Huntington.) Area of map is 50 by 44 miles. The roads follow the valleys between the ridges.

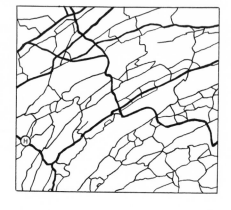

Stone Walls and Agriculture: Works of man in clearing the land and in agriculture are extensive. The many stone walls of New England are built of the numerous glacial boulders which initially covered the land in that region.

Terracing and contour plowing emphasize hill outlines and shapes, especially as seen from the air.

Irrigation ditches are often present in arid to semiarid regions. They differ from natural rivers in that they flow along a hillside in artificial channels rather than straight down a slope as in natural streams.

FIG. 33–4.
CONTOUR PLOWING. Texas.

Lakes: Many rivers have been dammed for power, irrigation purposes, or flood control, so that many lakes have been produced where there were none before. They are especially noticeable outside the glaciated areas, where lakes were essentially absent before man came.

FIG. 33–5.
ARROWROCK DAM, IDAHO.

Roads and Railroads: The extensive construction of railroads in the past and of roads now has necessitated considerable amounts of blasting and earth-moving, which has greatly modified the land surface in a number of places.

Road cuts give relatively steep slopes, thus promoting slumping, wash and soil creep in soft materials, and rockfalls and slides in more resistant rocks. Roads built across low-lying areas often cause swamps where adequate drainage has not been provided.

FIG. 33–6.
ROAD CUT AND TUNNEL. Coast Highway, California.

Pits, Quarries, Mines: Sand and gravel pits have been dug wherever these materials have been deposited by moving water, such as along the coast or in river beds. In glaciated areas, sand and gravel are often found in kame, esker, and outwash deposits.

Quarries which exploit a number of different kinds of rocks—granite, slate, and marble, for instance—are found in the more rugged parts of the country.

Mining, especially, has modified drastically the surface topography in a great many areas. Mine dumps range in size from a small pile of debris marking the entrance to a prospect hole to literally mountains of debris from which useful material has been extracted. Where deposits are extensive, enormous excavations hundreds of feet deep and covering many acres can be found; for example, the copper pit at Bingham Canyon, Utah, or the iron mines in the Lake Superior region.

Strip mining is especially noticeable in coal areas. Linear

gashes in the earth mark the surface exploitation of dipping layers of coal in the anthracite areas of the Appalachian Mountains. More extensive lateral removal marks the mining of more-nearly horizontal layers of coal. In the plateau areas of such states as West Virginia and Kentucky, the essentially horizontal coal layers outcrop on the sides of hills and have often been removed for some distance back into the slopes. This leaves a devastation of what appears to be newly cut roads which encircle the hills.

Dredging for gold in alluvial gravels is extensive, especially in Alaska and California. Dredged areas are marked by devastation and the dumping of gravel into wormlike segmented patterns.

FIG. 33–7.
STRIP MINING. Gillette, Wyoming. Coal is being mined here.

FIG. 33–8.
STRIP MINING. Kentucky. For scale, note vehicles at top.

FIG. 33–9.
OPEN-PIT COPPER MINE. Ajo,
Arizona.

FIG. 33–10.
MINE DUMPS. Michigan.

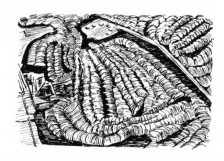

FIG. 33–11.
GOLD DREDGING. California.

Maps

DETAILED LANDFORM MAPS OF
THE UNITED STATES, WITH
BOUNDARY LINES OF
THE GEOLOGIC PROVINCES

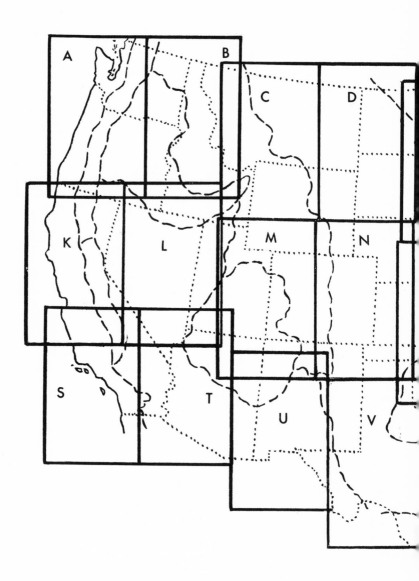

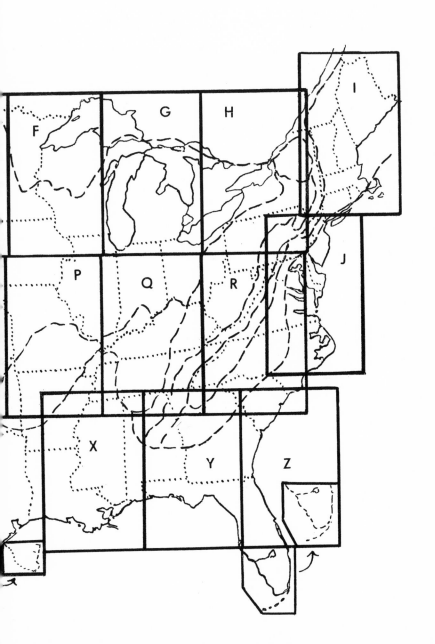

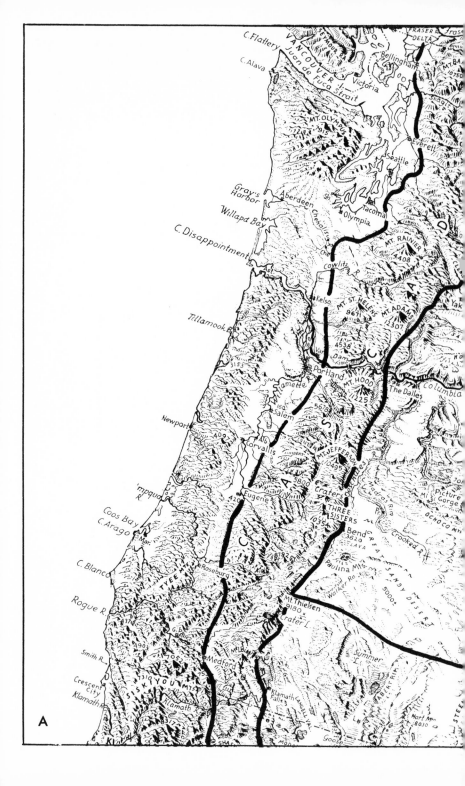

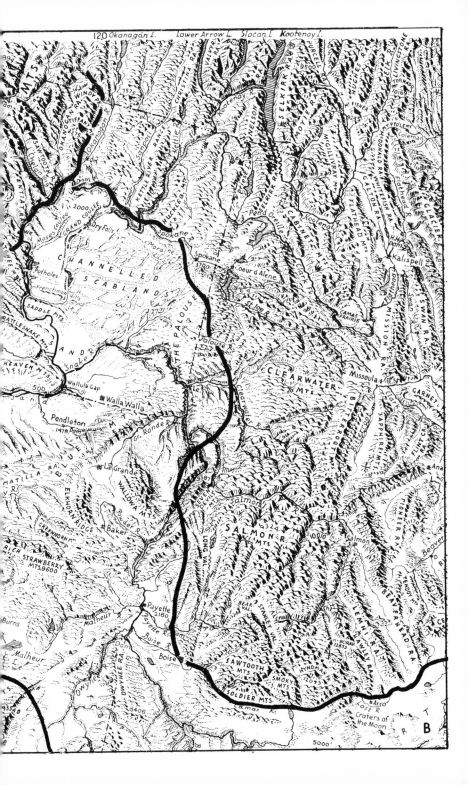

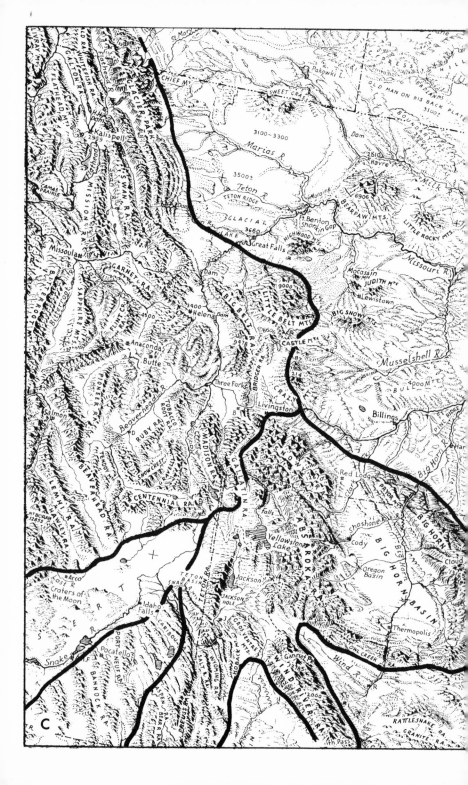

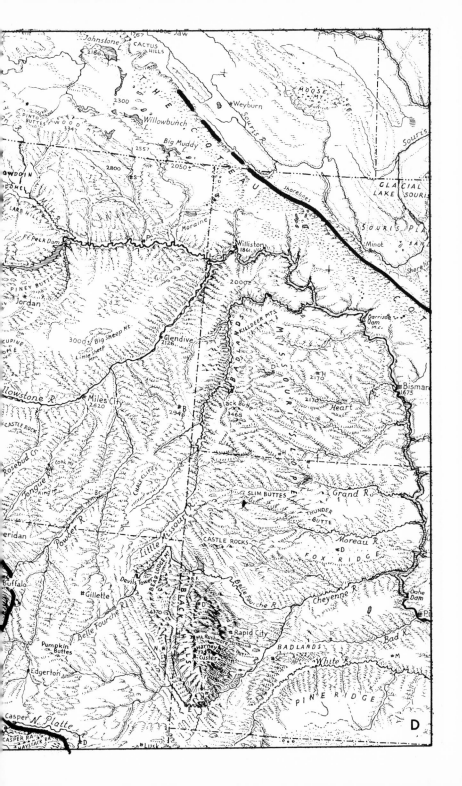

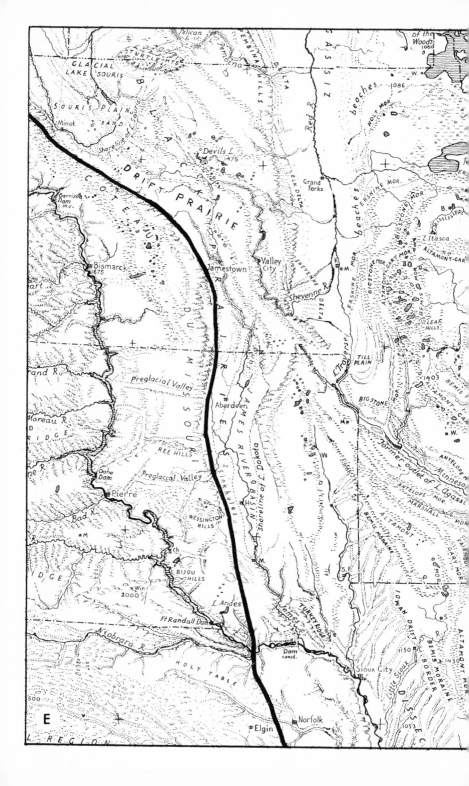

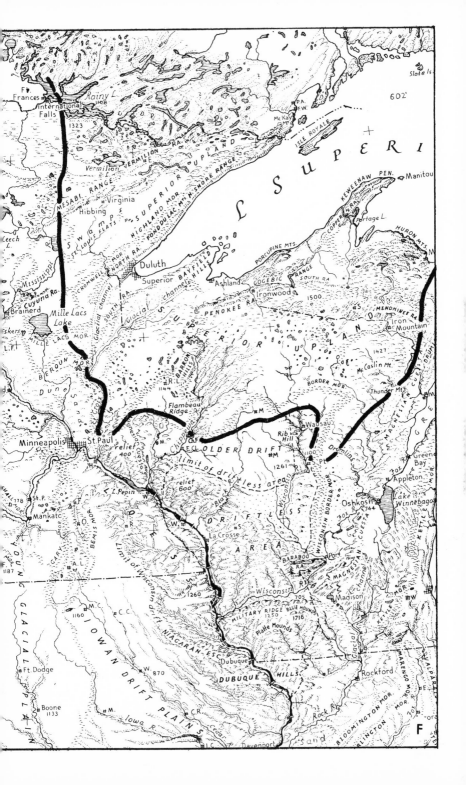

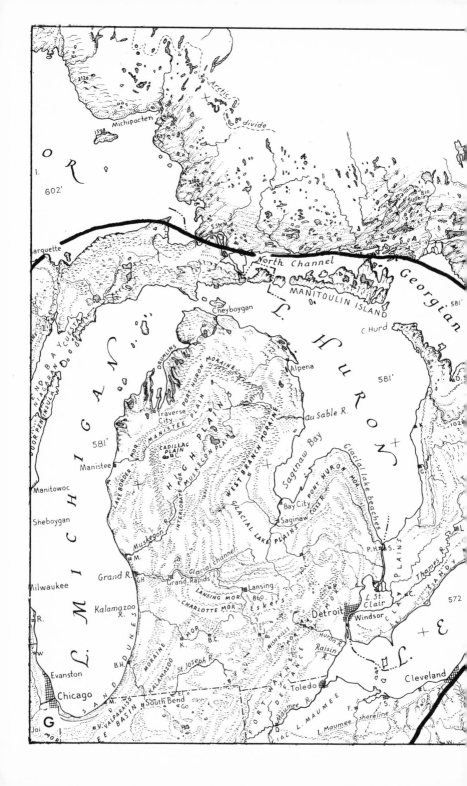

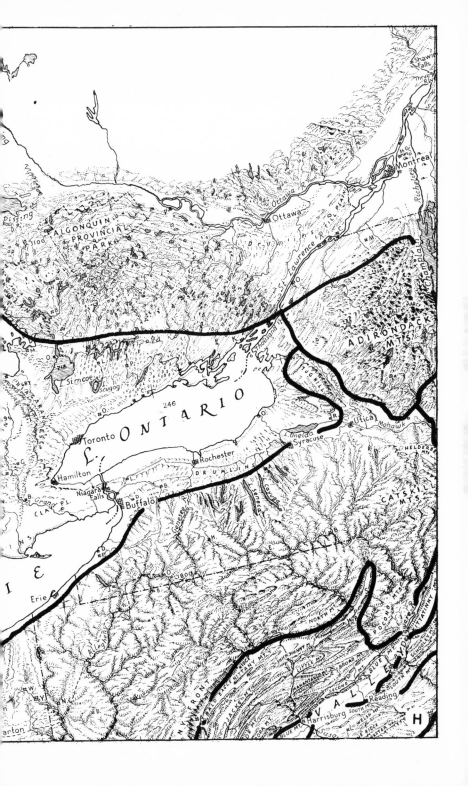

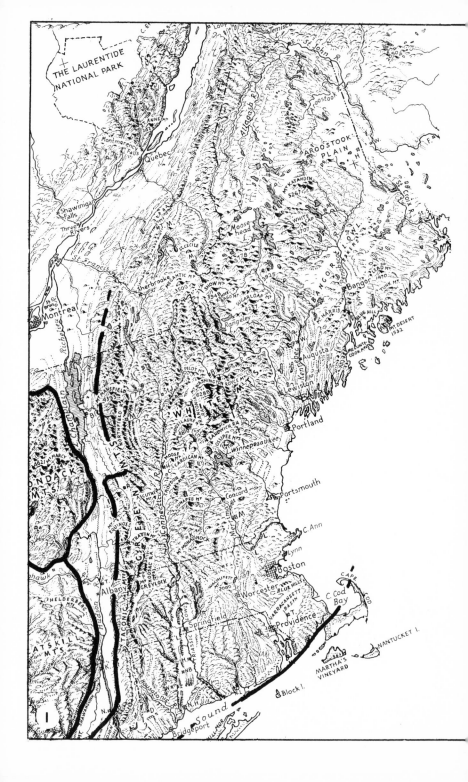

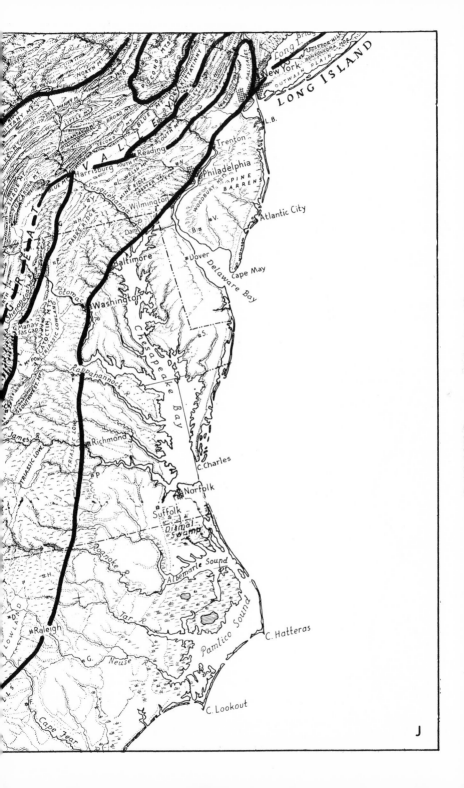

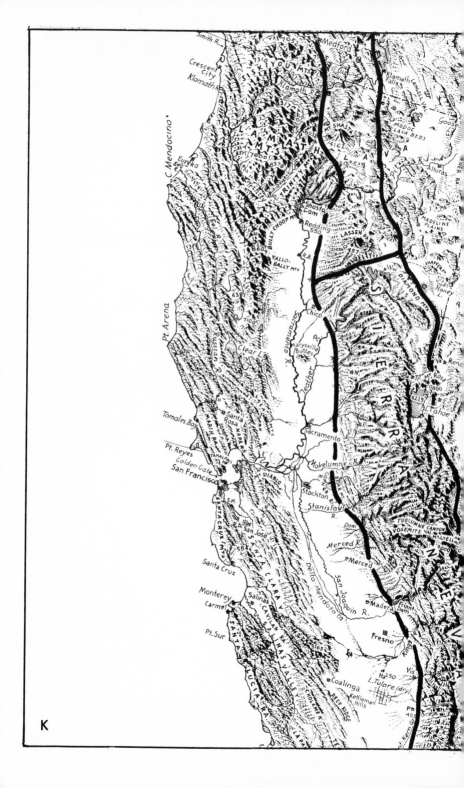

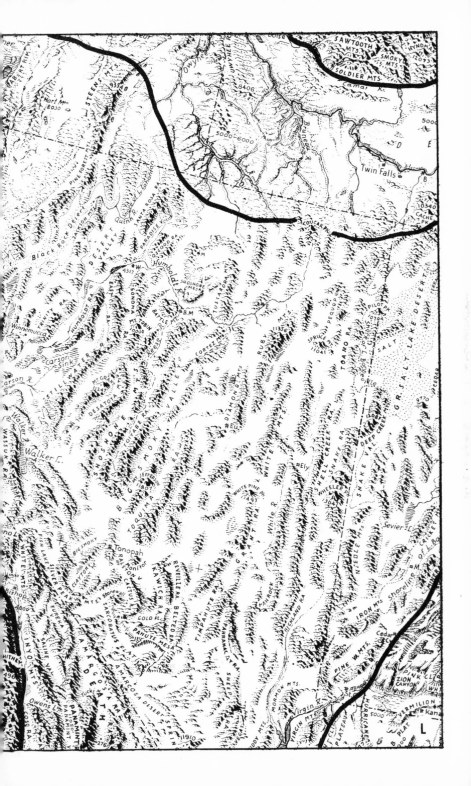

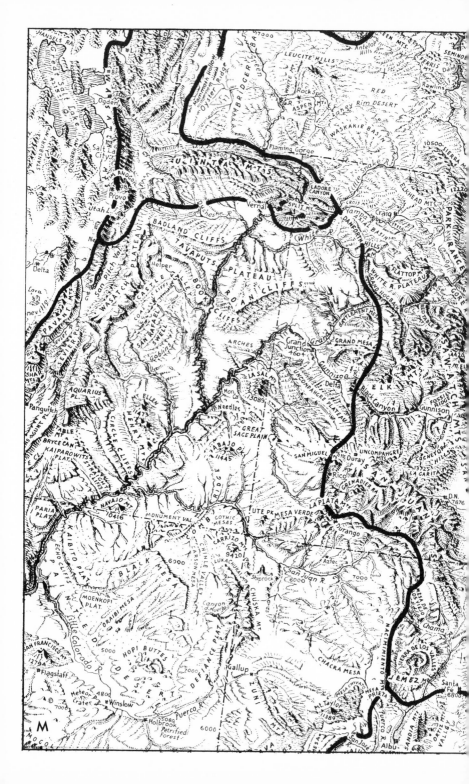

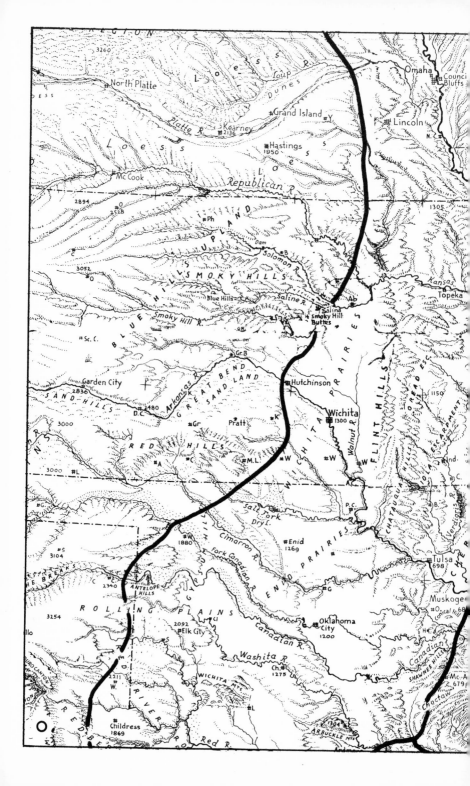

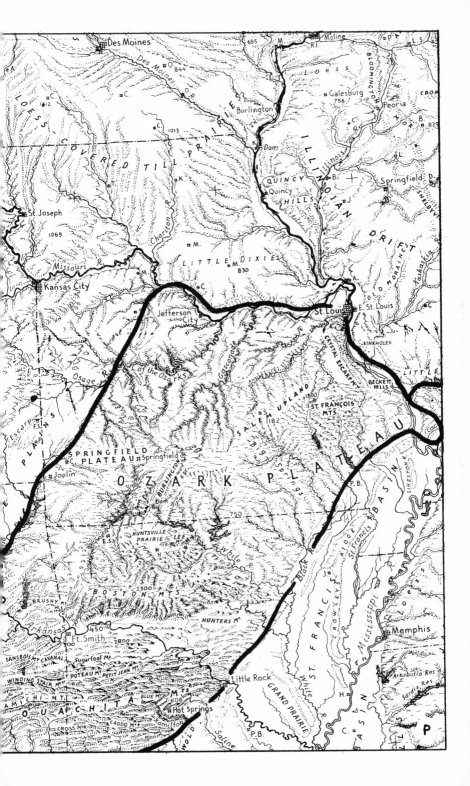

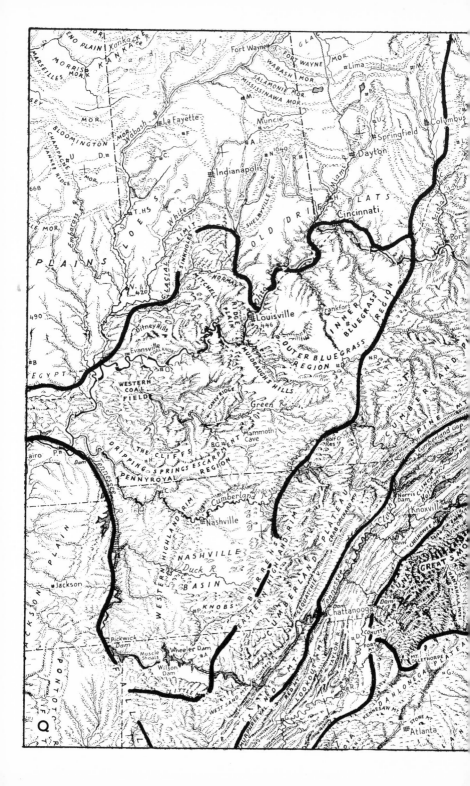

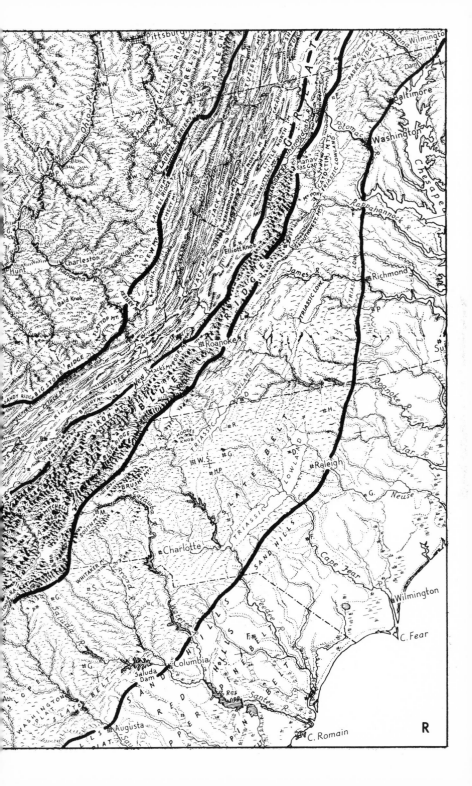

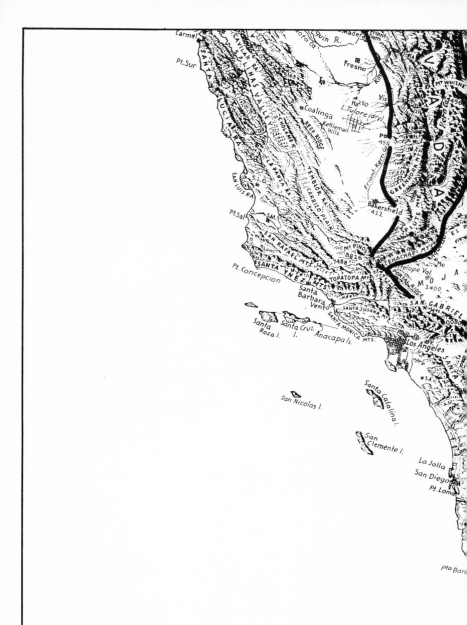

S

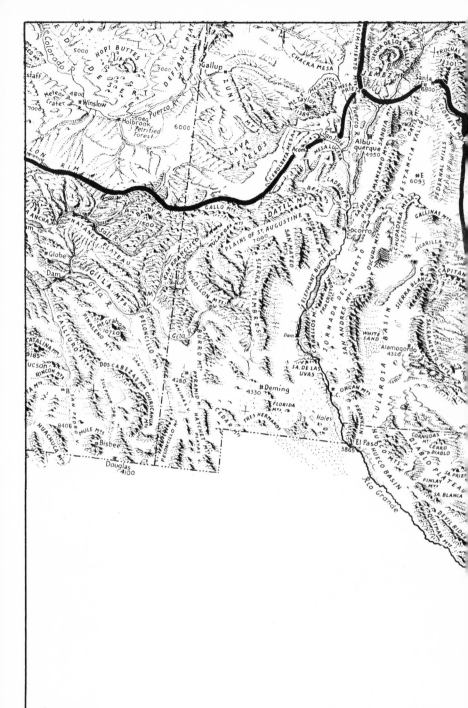

U

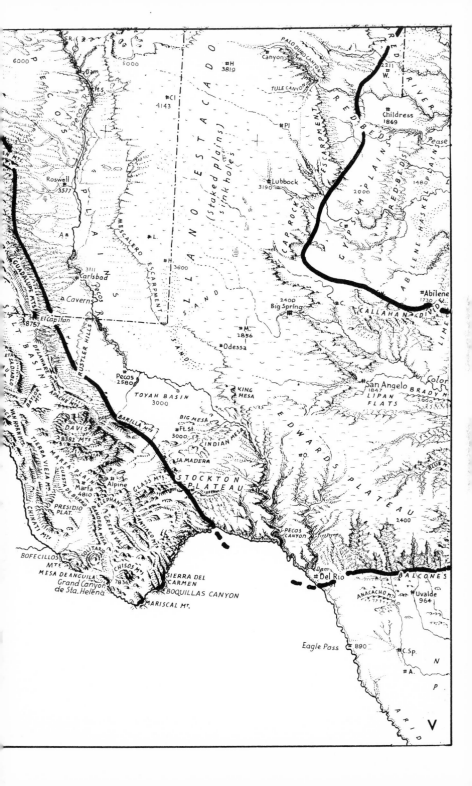

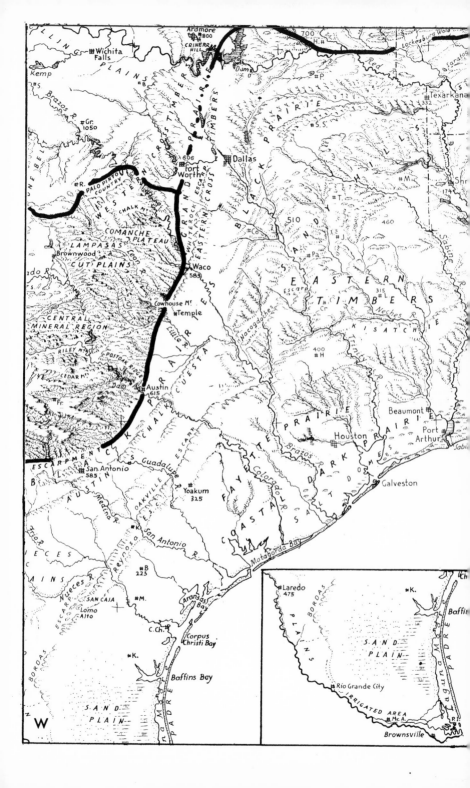

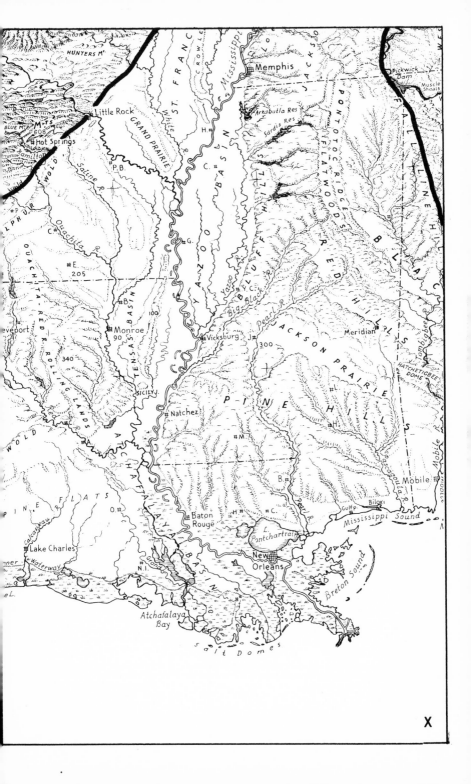

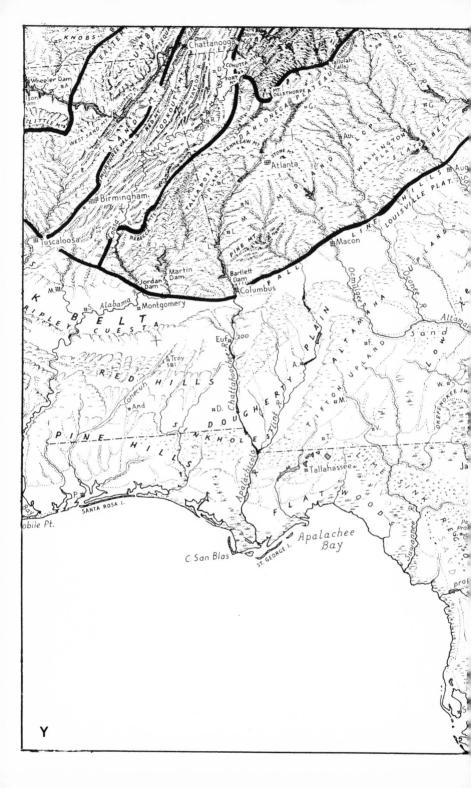

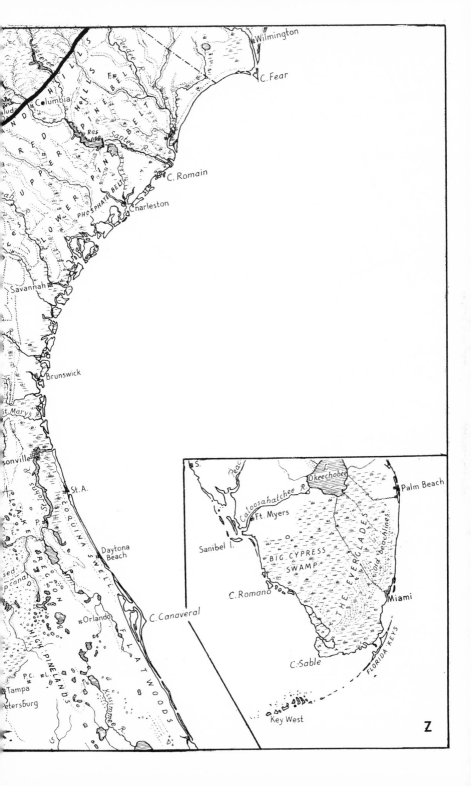

Landform Summary Chart

Major Geologic Processes and Associated
Features: Some Classic Examples and Locations

IGNEOUS ACTIVITY

Volcanic Cones

Types:
Spatter   (Craters of the Moon National Monument)
Cinder   (Amboy and Sunset Craters, Arizona)
Strato   (Mounts Hood, Shasta, Rainier)
Shield   (Kilauea and Mauna Loa, Hawaii)

Associated Features:
Caldera   (Crater Lake, Oregon)
Radial drainage pattern

Flows   (Columbia Plateau)

Lava Types:
Aa   Pahoehoe

Surface Features:
Caves   Collapse depressions
Tunnels   Tree molds

Columnar Jointing

Associated Features:
Fumaroles   Geysers
Hot springs   (Yellowstone National Park)

Intrusive Igneous Rock Bodies

  Batholith   (Idaho)
  Dike
  Sill   (Palisades of New York and New Jersey)

ROCK DEFORMATION AND MOUNTAIN BUILDING

Fault-Block Mountains   (Sierra Nevada, Grand Tetons)

  Associated Feature:
  Triangular facet on spur end (Wasatch Mountains, Utah)

Folded Mountains   (Ridge and Valley Province, Appalachian Mountains)

  Associated Features:
  Hogback   Water gap
  Synclinal ridge   Wind gap
  Anticlinal valley   Trellis drainage pattern

Domes   (Black Hills, South Dakota)

  Associated features:
  Cuesta
  Hogback

Basins   (Michigan Basin)

  Associated feature:
  Cuesta

Vertical Uplift   (Colorado Plateau)

  Associated features:
  Dendritic drainage pattern
  Mesa
  Cliff and bench topography

WEATHERING AND EROSION

Weathering

Spheroidal boulders
Exfoliation dome   (Yosemite Valley area)

Streams

Patterns:
Dendritic   (Mississippi River system)
Trellis   (Central Pennsylvania)
Rectangular   (Adirondack Mountains)
Contorted   (Coast of Maine)
Fault line   (San Andreas, California)
Radial: outward flowing   (Cascade Mountains)
Radial: inward flowing   (Sinkhole region of Tennessee)

Valley Profiles:
V-shaped
Flood plain   (Mississippi River)
U-shaped   (Crawford Notch, New Hampshire)
U-shaped with a flat floor   (Yosemite Valley)

Young River Features:
V-shaped valley
Falls and rapids
Potholes
Plunge pools
Alluvial fan   (Death Valley, California)

Flood Plain River Features:

Meanders	Natural levee
Oxbow lake	Delta
Point bar	Braided pattern

Rejuvenated River Features:
Terraces
Incised meanders

Ground Water in Limestone Areas

Erosional Features:
Sinkhole
Disappearing stream
Cave
Karst topography

Depositional Features:
Stalactite
Stalagmite
Pillar
Terraces

Wind

Erosional Features:
Deflation hollows   Desert pavement
Blowouts in sand dunes   Ventifact

Depositional Features:
Sand dune shapes: Sand dune features:
  Irregular   Ripple marks
  Barchan   Windward slope
  Parabolic   Slip face
Loess

Glaciers

Erosional Features:
U-valley   Horn
Cirque   Arête
Fjord   Finger lake
Hanging valley   *Roche moutonnée*
Tarn   Striations and grooves

Depositional Features of Till:
Moraine:
  End   (terminal)   Ground
  Medial   Interlobate
  Lateral
Drumlin   (central New York State)
Erratic
Kettle Hole

Depositional Features of Glacial Meltwaters:
Outwash plain   (South side of Long Island)
Lake deposit   (Lake Agassiz, North Dakota–Minn.)
Kame
Esker
Kettle hole

Permafrost Features   (*Alaska*):
Solifluction lobe   Ice-wedge polygons
Stone polygons   Pingo
Stone stripes   Patterned ground

Waves and Currents

Erosional Features   (*Pacific Coast*):
Cliff   Cave
Stack   Raised terrace
Arch

Depositional Features:
Beaches:
    Along shore   Offshore
    Bay-mouth
Spit
Tombolo
Beach details:
    Ripple marks   Rill marks
    Swash marks   Cusps

Shapes of Shorelines:
Drowned dendritic pattern   (Chesapeake Bay)
Drowned contorted pattern   (Coast of Maine)
Drowned fault-controlled lowland   (Point Reyes, California)
Drowned glacial topography
    Drumlins   (Boston Harbor)
    Moraines   (Long Island)
    U-valley   (Fjord coast of Alaska)
Delta   (Mississippi River)

Gravity Alone:

Rockfalls	Soil creep
Landslides	Solifluction lobe
Talus slope	

Further Reading

ATWOOD, W. W. *The Physiographic Provinces of North America.*
Boston: Ginn and Company, 1940.

An excellent discussion of the various geologic provinces of the country.

BULLARD, F. M. *Volcanoes.* Austin, Texas: University of Texas Press, 1962.

Much about volcanoes. Very readable.

DYSON, J. L. *The World of Ice.* New York: Alfred A. Knopf, Inc., 1962.

The way glaciers develop, and the landscape features which are associated with their activities.

MATHER, K. F. *The Earth Beneath Us.* New York: Random House, Inc., 1964.

Superlative illustrations of a great variety of landforms and a discussion of their origins.

MATTHES, F. E. *The Incomparable Valley.* Edited by F. M. Fryxell. Berkeley: University of California Press, 1950.

The geologic story of Yosemite Valley. A classic.

MATTHEWS, W. H., III. *A Guide to the National Parks: Their Landscape and Geology.* Vols. I and 2. Garden City, N.Y.: Natural History Press, 1968.

LOBECK, A. K. *Things Maps Don't Tell Us.* New York: The Macmillan Company, 1956.

A provocative discussion of how geologic history and rock structure can be inferred from a study of maps.

SCHUBERTH, C. J. *The Geology of New York City and Environs.* Garden City, N.Y.: Natural History Press, 1968.

SHELTON, J. S. *Geology Illustrated.* San Francisco: W. H. Freeman and Company, 1966.

A superb pictorial presentation of the structure and origin of landscape features.

SHIMER, J. A. *This Sculptured Earth.* New York: Columbia University Press, 1959.

An introduction to landforms and their origin.

STRAHLER, A. N. *A Geologist's View Of Cape Cod.* Garden City, N.Y.: Natural History Press, 1968.

THORNBURY, W. D. *Regional Geomorphology of the United States.* New York: John Wiley & Sons, 1965.

A well-illustrated systematic presentation of the geologic provinces.

WILLIAMS, H. *Crater Lake: The Story of Its Origin.* Berkeley: University of California Press, 1954.

Well illustrated. Written for the layman.

INDEX

Absaroka Mountains, 81, 84
Adirondack Mountains, 25, 31, 41–43, 51, 69, 214
Agathla, 97
Alabama, 13, 16, 27
Alaska, 123–31, 162, 167, 182, 214, 227
  Arctic Coastal Plain, 123, 124, 130, 131, 214
  Brooks Range, 123, 124, 128, 130, 131
  Interior Province, 123, 124, 128–30
  Pacific Mountain System, 123–27, 128
Alaska Range, 124, 127, 128
Albemarle Sound, 8, 10
Alcova, 79
Aleutian Islands, 124
Aleutian Region, 123
Allegheny Front, 27, 31, 34
Anchorage, 124
Appalachian Mountains, 151, 227
Appalachian Plateau, 3, 4, 16, 26, 30–34, 44, 48
Appalachian Ridge and Valley Region, 68
Appalachian Valley. *See* Great Valley
Arbuckle Mountains, 57
arches, 204
Arctic Coastal Plain, 123, 124, 130, 131, 214
arêtes, 159
Arizona, 89, 97
Arkansas, 14, 68
Arkansas Valley, 68
Atchafalaya River, 14, 15
Attu Island, 124
Austin, 15

Balcones Escarpment, 15, 59
Balcones Fault, 15
barchans, 194
Basin and Range, 64, 72, 88, 98, 103, 104–109, 110, 217, 219
Bastrop Hills, 14
bay-mouth bar, 186
beaches, 185, 186–87
Bear Butte, 61
Bear Mountain, 26

Bear Tooth Mountains, 81
Bearpaw Mountain, 60
Bend, 103
Berkshire Hills, 36
Big Belt Mountains, 60
Big Cobbler, 17
Big Hollow, 78
Big Snowy Mountain, 60
Big Spring, 67
Bighorn Basin, 81
Bighorn Canyon, 79
Bighorn Mountains, 77, 79, 81
Bingham Canyon, 226
Bitterroot Mountains, 85
Bitterroot Valley, 85
Black Hills, 4, 59, 60–61
Bliss, 103
Blowing Rock, 23
Bluegrass Region, 44–45, 46
Blue Hills, 37
Blue Ridge, 4, 16, 17, 21–23, 35, 37
Book Cliffs, 95
Boston Basin, 36
Boston Bay, 40
Boston Harbor, 40, 182
Boston Mountains, 66, 67
Bowling Green, 47
Bridalveil Waterfall, 111
Bridger Basin, 78
Brooks Range, 123, 124, 128, 130, 131
Brushy Mountains, 17
Bryce Canyon, 95
Buena Vista Lake Basin, 117
Burlington Escarpment, 67
Buzzard Bays' Moraine, 9

Cairo (Ill.), 14
California, 107, 110, 113, 116, 117, 118, 119, 120, 128, 151, 217, 227
California Coast Range, 117
Canada, 31, 37, 48, 50, 56, 69, 71, 72, 85, 86, 124, 167
Canyon Lands, 95–96
Cape Cod, 7, 8, 9, 40
Capital Reef, 96
Caprock Escarpment, 59, 63
Carlisle, 21
Carlsbad Caves, 64
Carolina Bays, 11–12

Cascades, 98, 100, 103, 113–15, 124
Casper, 78
Castle Mountain, 60
Cataract Canyon, 95
Catskill Mountains, 25, 31
caves, 209–12
Cayuga Lake, 33
Cedar Breaks, 95
Central Lowlands, 4, 44, 48–57, 58, 59, 60
Central Mineral District, 64
Central Valley, 110
Channeled Scablands, 100
Chatham Strait, 127
Chehalis River, 116–17, 118
Chesapeake Bay, 8, 10
Chester Escarpment, 45
Chestnut Ridge, 34
Cheyenne River, 60
Chicago, 54
Chugach Mountains, 127
Cincinnati Arch, 44
Cincinnati Dome, 48
Cirque Peak, 111
cirques, 159
Clark Fork, 86
Clearwater Mountains, 85
cliffs, 196, 198–203
Coast Range, 124
coastal features, 182–90
    depositional, 186–87
    erosional, 185
    islands, 190
    shapes of coastline, 182–83
Coastal Plain, 3, 7–15, 16, 17, 44, 48, 59, 60
    Cape Cod to North Carolina, 8–10
    East Gulf Section, 13
    Florida, 12–13
    Mississippi River Alluvial Plain, 14–15
    North Carolina to Florida, 10–12
    West Gulf Section, 15
Coastal Trough, 123
Coeur d'Alene Mountains, 85
Colorado, 59, 63–64, 73, 75, 87
Colorado Front Range, 59, 75–76
Colorado Piedmont, 59, 76
Colorado Plateau, 3, 72, 88–97
    Canyon Lands, 95–96
    Grand Canyon Area, 89–92
    High Plateaus, 92–95
    Navajo Section, 96–97
    Southeastern Volcanic Area, 97
    Uinta Basin, 95
Colorado River, 89, 109

Colorado Spring, 64
Columbia Basin, 99
Columbia Plateau, 72, 98–103, 154
Columbia River, 86, 100, 101
Commerce, 14
cones, 152, 196, 219
Connecticut, 10, 36, 40
Connecticut River, 36, 40
Cook Inlet, 123
Coosa River, 25
Copper River Lowland, 124
Coteau du Missouri, 60
Cowlitz River, 116–17
Crater Lake, 113, 115
Crawford Pass, 38
Crazy Mountains, 60
Crowley's Ridge, 14
Cumberland Plateau, 34
Cumberland River, 25, 46

Death Valley, 107–109
Deerfield, 40
Delaware Bay, 8
Del Norte, 77
Deschutes River, 103
desert forms, 191–95
Detroit, 54
Devil's Backbone, 115
Devil's Gate, 79
Devil's Golf Course, 107–108
Diamond Head, 133
Dixville Pass, 38
Dripping Springs Escarpment, 45, 47
drumlin, 164
dunes, 193–94

East Bahia Honda Key, 13
Edwards Plateau, 63
Elizabeth Islands, 9
Endless Caverns, 27
Eureka Springs, 67
Everglades, 12

Fall Line, 17
Fall Zone, 17
Faults, 150–51, 196
Findley Ridge, 19
Finger Lakes, 33, 214
Flathead Valley, 85
Flattop Mountain, 76
Flattop Peneplain, 87
flood plain, 179
Florida, 10, 12–13
Florida Keys, 13
flows, 154–55
Folded Appalachian Mountains, 151

folds, 145
Fond du Lac, 53
Franconia Pass, 38
Front Range, 76
fumeroles, 155

Gallup, 97
Galveston, 15
Garden of the Gods, 64
Georgia, 17, 19, 21, 29
glaciated landscapes, 159–68
    areas of permafrost, 167
    ice sheets, 159, 162–65
    ice streams, 159–62
Glacier National Park, 86
Glen Canyon, 95
Goshen Hole, 61
Grand Canyon, 89–92, 170, 197
Grand Coulee, 100–101
Grand Teton Mountain, 81
Grand Teton Mountains, 81–82
Great Falls, 60
Great Gulf Ravine, 38
Great Lakes, 54, 71
Great Plains, 48, 49, 58–64, 72, 75, 76, 77, 81, 87, 124
    High Plains area, 60, 61–63, 64
Great Sage Plain, 95–96
Great Salt Lake, 107, 217
Great Sandy Desert, 103
Great Valley, 4, 23, 25, 27–29, 37
Great Valley (Calif.), 117
Green Bay, 50, 54
Green Mountains, 25–26, 37
Green River, 46
Green River Basin, 78, 81
ground water, 209–12
Gulf of California, 109
Gunnison River, 76

Hagerstown River, 25
Hanaupah Fan, 107
Hanging Hills, 40
Harbor Hill Moraine, 10
Harney Peak, 61
Hawaii, 132, 136
Hawaiian Islands, 132–36
Helderberg Mountains, 31
Helena (Ark.), 14
Hell's Half Acre, 78
Henry Mountains, 96
High Plains, 60, 61–63, 64
High Plateaus, 92–95
Highland Rim, 45
Highlands, 99, 101
Highwood Peak, 60

hills, 196
Hoback Mountains, 82
Holyoke Ranges, 40
horns, 159
Hualalai, 133
Hudson River, 16, 25, 26, 31
Huntington Ravine, 38
Hurricane Fault, 92
Hurricane Ledge, 92

Idaho, 85, 98, 101
Idaho Batholith, 85
ice sheets, 159, 162–65
ice streams, 159–62
igneous rock, 139–41
igneous rock landscapes, 152–58
    cones, 152
    flows, 154–55
    intrusives, 156
Illinois, 14, 49, 52, 56
Illinois Basin, 49
Imperial Valley, 109, 119
Indiana, 45, 57
Interior Highlands, 65–68
Interior Low Plateau, 44–47, 50
Interior Lowlands, 49, 59
Interior Province, 123, 124, 128–30
    intrusives, 156
Iowa, 56
islands, 190

Jackson Hole, 81–82, 84
Jackson Lake, 82
James River, 8
Jemez Mountains, 76
Jenny Lake, 82
John Day Basin, 101
joints, 150, 151, 196
Judith Mountains, 60

Kaaterskill Creek, 31
Kahoolawe, 132
Kansas, 52, 59, 64
karst topography, 209
Kauai, 132
Kenai Mountains, 127
Kentucky, 34, 44, 46, 47, 227
Kentucky River, 46
Kern River, 117
Kettle Moraine, 54
Kettleman Hills, 117
Key West, 13
Kilauea, 133
King Ravine, 38
Kings Mountains, 17
Kings Peak, 81

Kittatinny Mountain, 26
Klamath Mountains, 116, 117, 118–19
Knobstone, 45
Kodiak Island, 127
Kohola, 133
Kuskokwim River, 128

Labyrinth Canyon, 95
Lake Agassiz, 56
Lake Bonneville, 107
Lake Erie, 50, 54
Lake Champlain, 25
Lake Coeur d'Alene, 86
Lake Manly, 108
Lake Michigan, 50, 54, 56
Lake Okeechobee, 12
Lake Ontario, 31, 53
Lake Placid, 43
Lake San Cristobal, 76
Lake Superior, 71, 226
   Lowlands, 56
   Uplands, 51, 56
Lake Tahoe, 111
Lake Winnebago, 53
Lake Winnemucca, 107
lakes, 213–18
   artificial, 214
   basins, 217
   glacial, 214
   of volcanic origin, 216
Lanai, 132
Laramie Basin, 78
Laramie Mountains, 73, 76, 77, 79
Laramie River, 79
Laurel Hill, 34
lava, 154–55
Lava Plains, 99, 101, 103
Lebanon River, 25
Leigh Lake, 82
Lexington (Ky.), 44, 46
limestone caves, 209–12
Little Belt, 60
Little Missouri River, 60
Little Rockies, 60
Llano Estacado, 63
Long Island, 9–10, 165, 182
Long Island Sound, 10, 40
Longs Peak, 75
Los Angeles, 117
Los Angeles Basin, 120
Louisiana, 15
Loveland, 76
Lowland, 124
Luray Cavern, 27
Lynn Beach, 40

Macon Ridge, 14
Maine, 37, 38, 190
Malaspina Glacier, 127
Mammoth Cave, 47
Mammoth Hot Springs, 84, 212
Manhattan, 17
man–made landscape features, 223–28
   lakes, 214, 225
   pits, quarries, mines, 226–27
   road patterns, 223
   roads and railroads, 225–26
   stone walls and agriculture, 224–25
Marble Canyon, 95
Martha's Vineyard, 40
Maryland, 26
Marysville Buttes, 117
Massachusetts, 37, 38, 40
Massanutten Caverns, 27
Massanutten Mountain, 27
Maui, 132
Mauna Kea, 133
Mauna Loa, 133
Medicine Bow Mountains, 73
Merced River, 111
Meriden, 40
metamorphic rock, 139, 145–48
Meteor Crater, 92
Mexico, 7, 15
Michigan, 53
Michigan Basin, 49
Middle Park, 76–77, 87
Middle Park Basin, 75
Middle Rockies, 73, 77, 79–84
Middletown, 40
Minnesota, 56, 86
Mississippi, 14
Mississippi River, 14–15, 54, 170
Missoula, 85–86
Missouri, 14, 59, 60, 67
Missouri Escarpment, 59, 60
Missouri River, 59, 60
Mohawk River, 31
Molokai, 132
Mono Craters, 111
Mono Lake, 107, 111, 217
Monomoy, 9
Montana, 59, 60, 85, 86
Montauk Point, 10, 182
Moon National Monument, 101–103
moraines, 162, 163
Moses Coule, 100–101
Mount Adams, 114
Mount Bernard, 111
Mount Ellen, 96
Mount Ellsworth, 96
Mount Evans, 75

Mount Glacier, 114
Mount Hillers, 96
Mount Hood (Ore.), 113
Mount Hood (Wash.), 114
Mount Jefferson, 113
Mount Langley, 111
Mount Lassen, 113, 114
Mount McKinley, 124
Mount Mansfield, 37
Mount Marcy, 41
Mount Mazama, 115
Mount Mitchell, 21
Mount Monadnock, 37
Mount Olympus, 118
Mount Rainier, 114
Mount Saint Helens, 113–14
Mount Shasta, 113, 114–15
Mount Shastina, 115
Mount Spurr, 124
Mount Sugarloaf, 40
Mount Taylor, 97
Mount Tom, 40
Mount Wachusett, 37
Mount Washington, 37–38
Mount Whitney, 111
mountains, 219–22
Muldrough Hills, 45

Nantasket Beach, 40
Nantucket, 40
Narragansett Basin, 36
Nashville, 44–45, 65
Nashville Basin, 45
Nashville Dome, 44–45, 65
Natchez, 14
Natural Bridge (Va.), 17
Natural Tunnel (Va.), 27
Navajo Mountain, 96
Navajo Section, 96–97
Niagara Cuesta, 50
Niagara Falls, 50
Niagara River, 50
Niihau, 132, 136
Near Boulder, 64
Nebraska, 51–52, 59, 60, 61
Nevada, 107, 217
New England, 16, 26, 35–40, 51
New Hampshire, 37, 38
New Haven, 40
New Jersey, 10, 17
New Mexico, 64, 72, 73, 97
New York Harbor, 8
New York State, 31–34, 50, 53, 182, 214
Norfolk Basin, 36
North Carolina, 11–12, 17, 19

North Dakota, 49, 56, 59
North Park, 76–77, 87
North Park Basin, 75
Northern Rockies, 73, 85–86, 151

Oahu, 132, 133, 136
Obsidian Cliff, 84
Ogallala Formation, 61–62
Ogden, 82
Ohio, 33
Ohio River, 54
Oklahoma, 57
Old Lyme, 40
Olympic Mountains, 118
Olympics, 118
Ontario, 50
Oregon, 101, 103, 113, 115, 116–17, 118, 122, 124
Oregon Coast Ranges, 118
Orient Point, 10, 182
Ouachita Mountains, 65, 67–68
outwash plain, 165
Owena Valley, 107
Owl Creek Mountains, 79
Ozark Dome, 48
Ozark Plateaus, 65

Pacific Border, 116–22
Pacific Border Ranges, 123, 127
Pacific Coastline, 185
Pacific Mountain System, 123–27, 128
Pacific Ocean, 132
Painted Desert, 97
Palisades, 20
Palos Verdes Hills, 120
Palouse Soils, 100
Pamlico Sound, 8, 10
Paradox Valley, 96
Pecos River, 64
Peninsular Ranges, 118, 120
Pennsylvania, 21, 26–27, 33
Phantom Ship, 115
Phelps Lake, 82
Piedmont, 9, 10, 13, 16–20, 23, 25
Pikes Peak, 75
pillars, 205
Pine Ridge Escarpment, 60
Pink Cliffs, 92–95
Pinkham Pass, 38
pinnacles, 115
Platte River, 61
Pocono Mountains, 25
Point Arena, 119
"Potholes," 82
Potomac River, 17
Presidential Range, 37–38

Provincetown, 9
Puget Sound, 116, 122
Purcell Trench, 85, 86
Pyramid Lake, 107, 217

Rabbit Ears Range, 77
Reading, 17, 26
Red Valley, 61
Rhode Island, 40
Ridge and Valley, 16, 24–29, 30, 31, 35, 36. *See also* Great Valley
ridges, 196, 197
Rio Grande, 15, 77
river features, 170–81
    flood-plain rivers, 179
    river rejuvenation, 181
    stream patterns, 170–71
    young rivers, 177
Roan Cliffs, 95
Roanoke, 21, 23
rock sculpture, 196–208
    arches, 204
    cliffs, 196, 198–203
    hills, 196
    pillars, 205
    ridges, 196, 197
    rockfalls, 206, 219–20
    slopes, 196, 203
rock structures, 148–51
    faults, 150–51
    joints, 150, 151
    tilts and folds, 148
rock types, 139–48
rockfalls, 206, 219–20
Rocky Mountains, 4, 49, 59, 60, 64, 72–86, 88, 98, 124, 130, 151, 219
    Middle Rockies, 73, 77, 79–84
    Northern Rockies, 73, 85–86, 151
    Southern Rockies, 73–77, 79, 87, 219
    Wyoming Basin, 72, 73, 77–79, 81, 87
Rocky Mountain National Park, 76
Rocky Mountain Peneplain, 87
Rocky Mountain Trench, 85, 86
Ronkonkoma Moraine, 10

Sacramento River, 117
Saginaw Bay, 50
Saint Elias Mountains, 127
Saint François Mountains, 65, 66
Salem Plateau, 66, 67
Salmon River, 85
Salt Lake City, 82
Salt Mountains, 82
Salt Valley, 96
Salton Sea, 109
San Andreas Fault, 119–20, 151

San Andreas Lake, 120
San Bernardino Mountains, 120
San Francisco, 119, 120
San Francisco Bay, 117, 122
San Francisco Embayment, 119
San Francisco Mountain, 92
San Gabriel Mountains, 120
San Joaquin Valley, 117
San Juan Mountains, 77
San Juan River, 95, 96
San Luis Valley, 75, 77
San Miguel Island, 120
San Rafael Swell, 96
Sand Creek Canyon, 115
Sand Spit, 186
Sandwich Moraine, 9
Sangre de Cristo Mountains, 73, 77
Santa Cruz Island, 120
Santa Monica Mountains, 120
Santa Rosa Island, 120
Santa Ynez Mountains, 120
Sawtooth Mountains, 85
sedimentary rock, 139, 143–44, 148, 196
Seneca Lake, 33
Sequatchie Valley, 34
Sevier Lake, 107
Shawangunk Mountains, 26
Shenandoah Caverns, 27
Shenandoah River, 25
Sherman Peneplain, 76, 87
Shiprock, 97
Sicily Island, 14
Sierra Nevada, 110–12, 124
Silver Springs (Fla.), 12
slopes, 196, 203
"Slumgullion" Flow, 76
Snake River, 82, 101, 103
Snake River Plain, 98, 103
Snake River Valley, 103
South Carolina, 11–12
South Dakota, 60, 63
South Mountains, 17
South Park, 77, 87
South Park Basin, 75
Southeastern Volcanic Area, 97
Southern Rockies, 73–77, 79, 87, 219
Spanish Peaks, 64
Springfield Plateau, 66, 67
Steptoe Butte, 99
Stone Mountain, 19
Subsummit Peneplain, 87
Summit Peneplain, 87
Sunset Crater, 92
Superior Upland, 51, 56, 69–71
Susitna Valley, 123

swamps, 213
Sweetgrass Hills, 60
Sweetwater River, 79

Taconic Mountains, 25–26, 36, 37
Tehachapi Mountains, 117
Tennessee, 25, 29, 34
Teton Basin, 82
Texas, 15, 49, 60, 63
Thousand Springs, 103
Three Sisters, 113
tilts, 148
Tomales Bay, 120
tombolo, 186
Tower Junction, 84
Trail Ridge, 13
Transverse Ranges, 116, 118, 119, 120
Trenton, 17
Tuckerman Ravine, 38
Tulare Lake Basin, 117
Twin Falls (Id.), 103

Ubehebe Craters, 109
Uinta Basin, 95
Uinta Mountains, 79–81, 95
United States, geological subdivisions,
        3–6
Utah, 95–96, 107, 217, 226
Utah Lake, 107

Valles Caldera, 76
valleys, 159–80
Vermilion Cliffs, 92
Vermont, 37
Virginia, 12, 17, 26, 27
volcanoes and volcanic cones, 152, 190,
        196, 219. *See also* lava

Wabash River, 54, 57
Walkill River, 25
Wasatch Mountains, 81, 82–84
Washington, 113, 116–17, 118, 124
Watchung Mountains, 20
water, ground, 209–12
Watkins Glen, 33
West Virginia, 26, 34, 227
Wet Mountain Valley, 75
White Cliffs, 92–95
White Mountains, 37–39
White River, 60
White Sands National Monument,
        105–106
Wichita Mountains, 57
Willamette River, 117
Willamette Valley, 116
Wind River Basin, 79
Wind River Canyon, 79
Wind River Mountain, 79
Wisconsin, 52, 53, 56
Wisconsin Driftless Area, 56
Wizard Island, 115
Wrangell Mountains, 127
Wyoming, 61, 73, 76, 79, 82
Wyoming Basin, 59, 72, 73, 77–79, 81,
        87
Wyoming Mountains, 82

Yakutat Bay, 127
Yellowstone Park, 84, 212
Yellowstone Plateau, 84
Yosemite Valley, 111
Yosemite Waterfall, 111
Yukon River, 128

Zion Canyon, 95
Zuni Uplift, 97